NATURAL HISTORY OF CANADA # The Nature of Fish

Scientific consultants to the series: WALTER TOVELL, PhD, Director, Royal Ontario Museum; J. MURRAY SPEIRS, PhD, Department of Zoology, University of Toronto

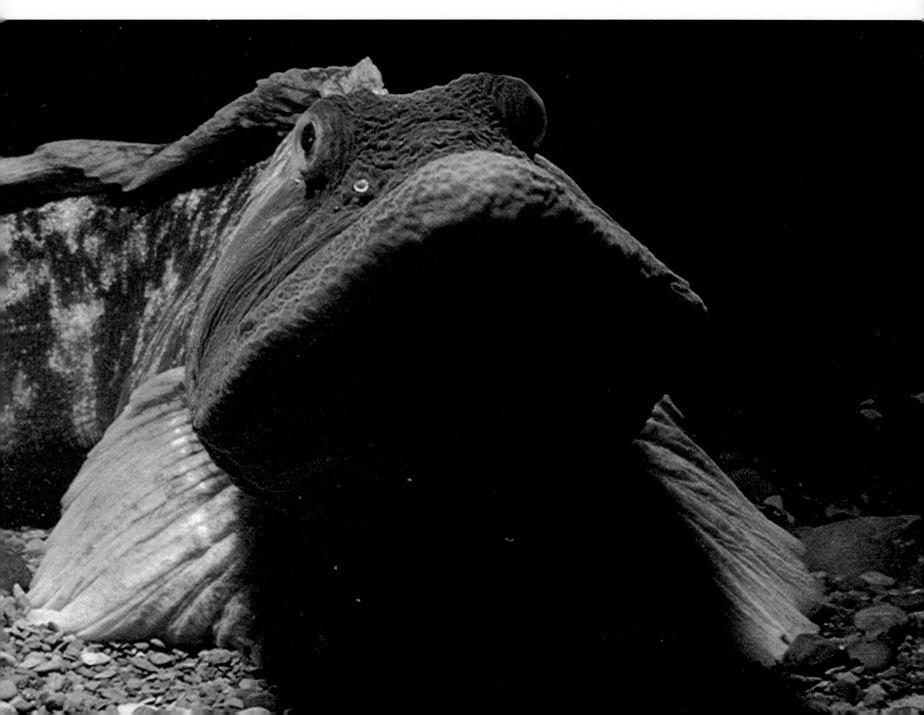

ISBN: 0-9196-4412-0

Natural Science of Canada Limited
58 Northline Road, Toronto, Ontario   M4B 3E5

Publisher: Jack McClelland
Managing Director: William Belt
Editor: Jennifer Glossop
Assistant Editor: Betty Kennedy
Art Director: Robert Young

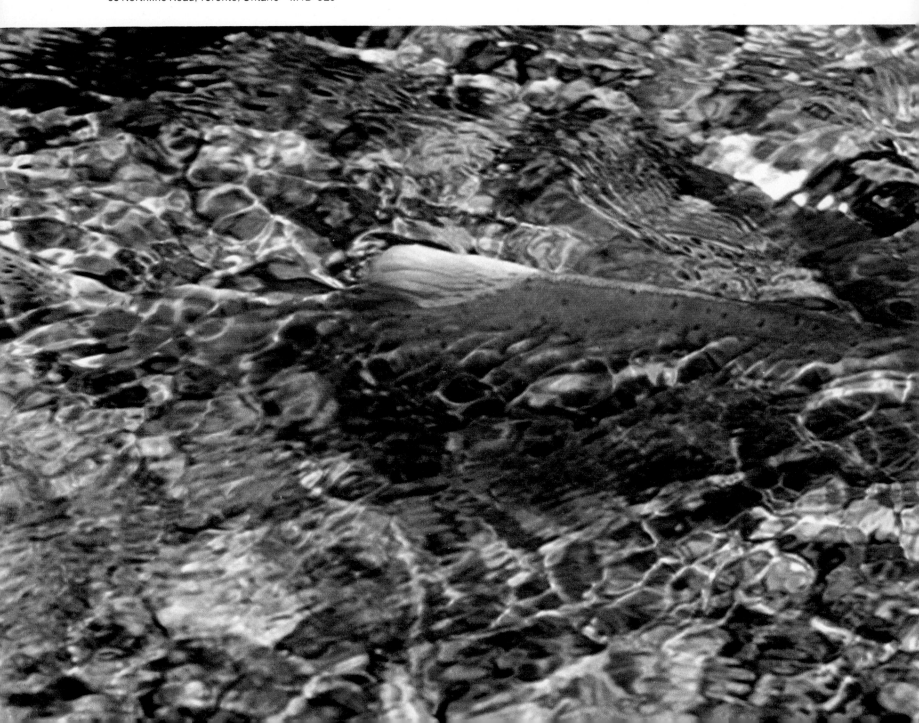

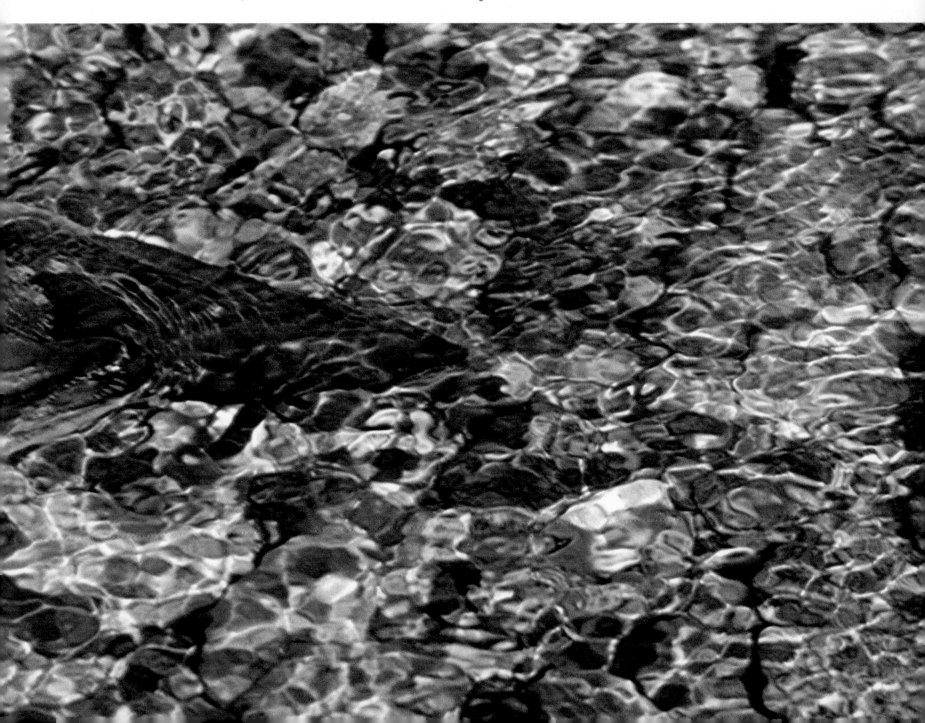

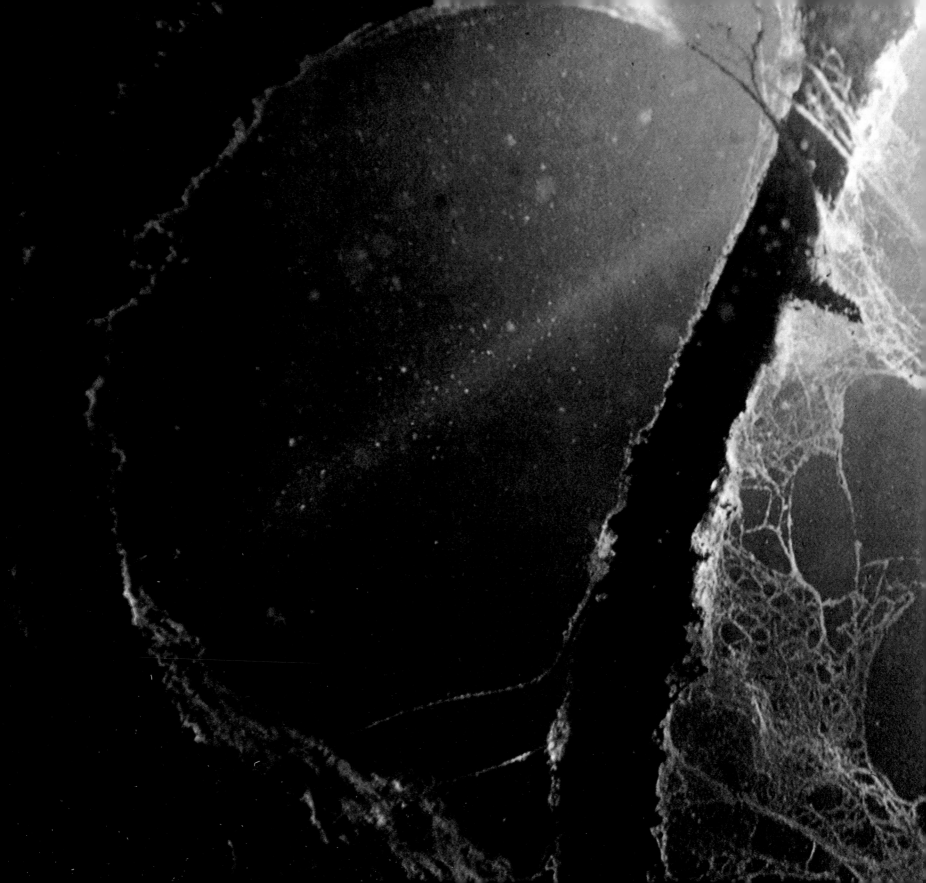

CONTENTS

INTRODUCTION

Fishes should have a special place in the hearts of Canadians, for it was the abundance of fishes, especially cod, that attracted European fishermen to our shores and so stimulated the development of settlement in eastern Canada. Our abundant lakes and rivers, ideal habitats for freshwater fishes, are unparalleled in a world already acutely aware of the value of fresh water.

Fishes are unique among the food resources of the world for, unlike cattle, poultry, or wheat, the fishes that are gathered commercially, or are angled, are not cultivated but are 'wild.' They are produced by nature, not by man and, thus, are 'God-given' rather than 'man-made.'

In addition to their commercial uses, fishes are used as laboratory specimens for studies in comparative anatomy, and as living specimens for studying behaviour in psychology and biology courses. Living fishes are also used to indicate the presence of toxic substances in natural waters.

As laboratory animals, fishes are exceedingly useful because they are so easily maintained. Various factors of the aquatic environment, such as temperature, salinity, and carbon dioxide and oxygen concentrations, can be rather easily controlled, and their effects measured. A great deal of this kind of work has been done on fishes, forming a broad and useful stock of information on the physiology of fishes in particular and in life processes generally.

An important role is also served in medical research. For example, the lowly hagfish has received considerable attention from bio-medical specialists because it is useful in heart-function studies and, apparently, lacks heart nerves. It also lacks a thymus and does not form anti-bodies – features that make it an attractive organism for research.

Fishes are the earliest, or the oldest, of living vertebrates, as you will learn from the following pages. But, besides having the longest pedigree of all the vertebrates, they also dominate the major portion of the earth's surface, since 70 per cent of the surface is water. They also enjoy the greatest vertical range, for they are known to live in lakes nearly three miles above sea level in the Andes Mountains, and in oceanic depths nearly seven miles below sea level in the deepest parts of the Pacific.

To occupy such a vast domain, fishes have become adapted to ways of life that tax the imagination. There are flyingfishes, swordfishes, pipefishes, goatfishes, parrotfishes, cavefishes, porcupinefishes, butterflyfishes, catfishes, lizardfishes, lan-

WAYLAND DREW   DON BALDWIN   ALAN EMERY   WAYNE McLAREN   ROBERT COLLINS

ternfishes, to name only a few of the hundreds of families. In each case cited above, the name is appropriate, for flying-fishes have greatly expanded pectoral fins that permit them to glide through the air for distances of a hundred yards or more; swordfishes have a long sword-like snout that they use, cutlass-like, to catch food; cavefishes live in caves; and lanternfishes have numerous light organs on their bodies.

Of all the fishes, however, there is one group that stands out from all the rest. I refer to the sharks, particularly the large predaceous ones, such as the requiem and mackerel sharks. These ancient fishes, that arose millions of years ago, have successfully resisted dominance by man. Although we have conquered the large mammals, and even threaten the very existence of polar bears and the great whales, the sharks still move freely through their oceanic world. It is sobering to think that in areas where sharks abound we must build heavy mesh fencing to protect bathers. Indeed, the shark, of all predators, is the most feared by man and, hopefully, will remain so. They may yet force us to respect the magnificence, power, and durability of the natural world.

W. B. SCOTT
Royal Ontario Museum

THE AUTHORS

WAYLAND DREW is a free-lance writer and amateur naturalist. His recent work includes a novel, *The Wabeno Feast*, as well as essays on conservation for *Canadian Forum* and *Ontario Naturalist*. DON BALDWIN is presently a biology teacher at Upper Canada College. He is the author of many papers on ornithology and natural history. ALAN EMERY, PhD, is an Associate Curator, Department of Ichthyology and Herpetology at the Royal Ontario Museum. He has published scientific papers on the taxonomy, behaviour, and ecology of fishes. WAYNE McLAREN is a free-lance writer on environmental matters. He is currently a consultant for the new Metropolitan Toronto Zoo. ROBERT COLLINS has been a working journalist for the last twenty-four years. He is currently a contributing editor of *Reader's Digest* (Canada).

PART ONE
WHAT IS A FISH?

West coast Indians have many stories about salmon, but none shows their attitude more clearly than a legend from the Wolf Clan of the Tsimshians. According to this tale, some young men of the clan began to practise cruelty to animals, killing them more slowly than necessary and often torturing them and leaving them to die in agony. When the elders protested and warned against such wantonness, the young men scorned them, and the cruelty and waste continued. In due course, the clan journeyed to their traditional fishing grounds, a canyon far up the Nass River, to harvest the spawning salmon. No time was more important to the tribe, no place more hallowed by tradition, and no creature more honoured than the salmon. Yet even here the cruelty continued.

To the horror of the rest of the clan, the young men made living torches of trapped fish, slitting their backs, inserting firebrands, and releasing them to splash in the shallows until

In this painting, Spearing Salmon by Torchlight, *Paul Kane depicts the traditional native method of harvesting this plentiful crop during the spawning season in British Columbia.*

they died. After this, the elders knew that disaster would befall the clan, and later in the year when the earth began to shake and rumble as if beaten by superhuman drummers, they were not surprised.

'It is only the dead,' the young men said. 'It is the dead preparing for a feast.'

But the older people knew that the torture of the fish had outraged the deepest forces of nature. Before long, the mountains opened, the rivers ran with fire and the forests blazed, consuming villages and people. Of the offending Wolf Clan, few survived.

For the Tsimshians, as for other west coast tribes, fishing was the centre of life. The journals of early traders vividly recall the joy with which these Indians greeted the salmon runs. In a short time, enough food could be taken to last an entire year. So secure and wealthy were most of the coastal tribes that they had leisure for creative play – carving elaborate implements and decorations, designing lavish feasts and ceremonies. In sheer exuberance, their culture was one of the richest in Canada, and it all depended on the largess of the sea.

They shared the ancient traditions of fishermen. Very early in his evolution, even before he began to fashion tools, man turned his attention to the creatures of the waters around him. Perhaps at first he used his hands to scoop them out, much as a fishing bear will pluck salmon from the rapids, but soon he began to devise more cunning traps – barbed arrows, serrated spears, clusters of bone and wooden slivers; lures, traps, weirs, rawhide nets, and thorny baskets; and, of course, hooks designed either to pierce the body or to snag in the tissues of the mouth. In time, the first coastal Canadians armed themselves with harpoons and ventured out after aquatic mammals – the seal, the walrus, and the whale. For them, as for others who dwelt beside all the world's oceans, fish were the staple of life, worth the often great risks required to capture them.

Even in the best ships, man has always been vulnerable to the sea. Uncharted reefs loom up. Storms snap masts and crush hulls under tons of water. Icebergs reach out hidden talons. And, occasionally, boats are stove in by the monstrous flukes or foreheads of whales. Small wonder that the sea and its creatures hold a prominent place in man's collective imagination. Leviathan, the Kraken, the Loch Ness monster, and many other mythical creatures are evidence of our abiding awe and respect for the water's mysteries. Even today, despite our bathyspheres and sophisticated detection equipment, the ocean holds many surprises. What was it, for example, large enough to straighten out a three-foot iron hook at 200 fathoms? Or what was it that lay at 500 fathoms and sent an undecipherable signal when detected by sonic gear?

Grotesque is the word we sometimes use to describe those fishes that inhabit the abyss – grotesque, misshapen, horrible, with their trailing fins, their great eyes, their awesome teeth. Surely no living things are more remote from man than these. And yet, once we have understood that each of their strange characteristics is a meticulously evolved refinement, and that each of these fish is superbly adjusted to its extreme environment, then they become objects of fresh interest and respect.

For the ancient Chaldeans, the abyss held the key to wisdom. Ea, the fish-god who was one of their three major deities, was perfect and all-knowing. The Greeks retained this wise fish-god, calling him Oannes, and for both the Greeks and the Romans some fish carried a special significance. The dolphin (the mammal as well as the fish) symbolized persistence, love, and speed. The Sumerians also worshipped a fish god. In their mythology it was the Sublime Fish that saved man and his fellow mammals from the great flood, teaching them the necessary crafts, and counselling them to build an ark when all other gods had deserted them. From Indian mythology comes a similar story in which Vishnu, the supreme god of goodness and light, assumes the form of a fish to warn man of the approaching deluge.

Some scholars have suggested that early Christians adopted the fish as a cult signature because the first letters of the Greek for "Jesus Christ, Son of God, Saviour" (*Iesous Christos theou hyios soter*) spell *ichthys*, fish. The sign had a deeper significance than this, however. For centuries it had been used on amulets as a fertility symbol, and it therefore suggested the perpetuation of life itself. It also bore ancient connotations of godliness, perfection, and the cleansing power of water. Most important, *ichthys* represents a creature through which humanity glimpses another realm, a realm both generative and destructive, both intimate and mysterious.

For most of his history, man has thought of fishes in terms of their relationship to him. Only fairly recently, with the rise of taxonomy and evolutionary theory, has he begun to examine them with more objective interest, seeking to find the relationships among species, and between individual species and their environments.

Although sea monsters are usually associated with the dark ages, present-day Canadians still report sighting these serpents. A 'Sea-Hag' was reported off Vancouver Island in 1950. It was said to be capable of rearing its head four or five feet out of the water. Behind the head, the body looped around itself a number of times, making an estimate of its length difficult, although it was said to be thirty-five to forty feet in length. The publicity accorded such reports indicates man's curiosity about the mysteries of the sea.

1 TRUE FISH

What is a fish? The answer seems easy: a fish is any cold-blooded, gilled, scaly, aquatic vertebrate. But so diversified are the approximately 20,000 fish species that even this general definition cannot include them all. Some ocean-roving types like the tuna maintain a body temperature slightly higher than the surrounding water. Not all fishes have scales, and some spend so much time out of water that they seem to be more amphibian than aquatic. Migrating eels absorb oxygen through their skins from wet grass, and lungfish have so refined their breathing apparatus that they can live for months in dried mud. Yet both are fish. To complicate matters further, many creatures with *fish* in their names are not fish at all. Shellfish, for example, may be either molluscs like the oyster and the clam, or crustaceans like the lobster. The cuttlefish is a mollusc, the starfish is an echinoderm, and the jellyfish is a coelenterate – all are invertebrates and lack the basic requirements of fish.

True fish have flexible vertebrae composed of juxtaposed bony or cartilaginous components. They hold this characteristic in common with all the other forms of life that have evolved from them – amphibians, reptiles, birds, and mammals – for they are the oldest living vertebrates as well as the most numerous. The typical fish breathes by means of gills – fragile membranes which draw oxygen from the water. Its eyes have no lids. Its heart has only two chambers, as opposed to three in reptiles and four in mammals, and its blood is usually the same temperature as the surrounding water. Its skin is covered with a film of slippery, protective, healing mucus. It propels, balances, and brakes itself by means of fins.

Sharing these characteristics are creatures as dissimilar as the seahorse, the manta ray, the eel, and the sturgeon. In North American waters alone, there are about 2,200 species of fishes. Ichthyologists are not entirely agreed on all details of their classification, and the more specialized questions of fish taxonomy need not concern us.

LATERA

NARES

OPERCULUM

GILL OPENING

PECTORAL FIN

Common characteristics

There are many variations on the basic fish type, but all fishes share some characteristics. All are cold-blooded vertebrates, have fins or rudiments of fins, live in water, and respire by means of gills. The rainbow trout (above) has a familiar shape and characteristics. The seahorse (right), rather than ordinary scales, has rows of connected bony plates, a camouflage aid. It moves in a vertical position, propelled by its dorsal fin; its prehensile tail is finless. The rock fish (right centre), which spends much time on or near the bottom, vividly illustrates the intensity of coloration of some fishes. The ray (far right) has greatly enlarged pectoral fins with which it 'flies' through the water.

DORSAL FIN

ADIPOSE FIN

ANAL FIN

CAUDAL FIN

ANUS

PELVIC FIN

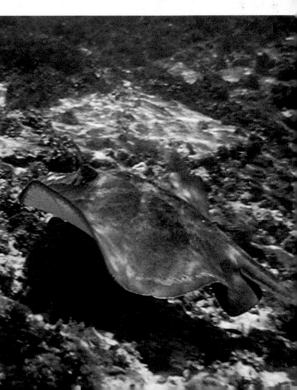

All living fishes can be divided into three broad categories. Most primitive are the Agnatha (Greek: *a* – without, *gnathos* – jaws), a class of which the lampreys and the hagfish are the only two living representatives. Both are found in Canadian waters, and both are parasitic carnivores. For thousands of years, the lamprey went no further inland than Lake Ontario, returning to the sea to spawn. In that time, a balance was struck between the populations of the lamprey and the fishes on which it fed. Then, at the end of the last century, the first lampreys found their way through the Welland Canal around Niagara Falls and into the rich feeding grounds of the other Great Lakes. Here they have become well established and have developed new breeding habits which have enabled them to remain in fresh water and to thrive at the expense of their victims. Their rasp-like tongues easily scrape away protective scales, and the anti-coagulant they inject into the wound is strong enough to dissolve the surrounding tissues. Few fish survive a lamprey attack.

The feeding habits of the other agnathan, however, are even more astonishing. The hagfish is an ocean dweller with a face like a crumpled football. It is found off both the east and the west coasts of Canada, ranging in depth between ten and 500 fathoms. Normally, the hagfish attacks sickly victims, invading their bodies through their gill apertures and suffocating them in mucus. It then proceeds to consume all internal organs and tissues, leaving only skin and bones. Clearly, these agnathans could not have survived if other fishes on which they depend had not evolved and adapted successfully. Their relatives, the armoured ostracoderms, became extinct many millions of years ago.

The lamprey (below), *an agnathan, is one of the most primitive of fishes. It has no jaws; its circular mouth, with which it clamps onto its prey, has horny teeth. The sand shark* (right), *a cartilaginous fish, has numerous protruding sharp teeth. The pike* (far right), *a more advanced form of predator, uses its powerful pointed teeth to catch other fish and small animals.*

The second major class of fishes consists of the skates, the rays, the sharks, and the chimaeras. These are Chondrichthyes, whose skeletons are made of cartilage. Although they have some agnathan characteristics, they are considerably more sophisticated, with efficient jaws and complex nervous and circulatory systems. Chondrichthyes are probably no older than bony fishes, but because their blood has the same salt content as the water in which they live, ichthyologists believe that they were the original inhabitants of the oceans and that bony fishes migrated seaward from lakes and rivers. The differences between the two types are significant. Unlike bony fishes, Chondrichthyes have neither gill covers nor air bladders, and their fertilization always takes place internally, using pelvic fins (called claspers) adapted for copulation. The scales of cartilaginous fishes are not tiny wafers of bone but rather modified teeth, or denticles, which form an abrasive covering for the body. A human swimmer could be badly scraped just by brushing against a shark. Finally, the intestines of cartilaginous fishes contain a winding membrane, similar to a spiral staircase, which slows the passage of food and guarantees maximum absorption.

The third and largest class is that of the Osteichthyes, the bony fishes, of which about 2,000 species are represented in North America. These fishes have found their way throughout the earth, adapting to an almost infinite variety of environments – water that is warm or cold, clear or murky, shallow or deep, salt or fresh, flowing or stagnant.

No fish enjoys an unlimited habitat. Temperature, depth, salt content, and other factors define the range for every species. Although some fishes are compulsive travellers (the tuna, for example, apparently never stops swimming, and by the time it is fifteen years old it has probably swum a million miles), still they will journey only through compatible environments. Consequently, one way of classifying fishes is by defining their habitats. Some fishes dwell close to shore in relatively shallow waters, and some, the neritic types, prefer various levels of the sloping continental shelves. Those that swim freely through the seas are pelagic (Greek: *pelagos* –

sea). If they drift on the ocean currents they are planktonic, deriving their name from the Greek word for wanderers. Bottom dwellers are benthic, and if they have adapted themselves to great depths they are bathypelagic. Few fishes cross the boundaries of these zones.

For most, however, the barrier between salt water and fresh water is the most formidable, although some species live comfortably in the river estuaries where the waters mix, and some anadromous species such as salmon pass from one type of water to the other to spawn. These fishes can make adjustments denied to others. The problem for most is that water tends to flow from a lower to a higher concentration of salt. Because their internal salinity does not match that of their surroundings, and because their skin is permeable to water, an osmotic process occurs. Most marine fishes are less salty than the sea. Without some form of regulation, they would tend to lose water, become dehydrated, and shrink. The technical word for their condition is *hypotonic*. They are therefore equipped with special cells in the gills which remove salt before the fish ingests water. *Hypertonic* freshwater species, on the other hand, have exactly the opposite problem. They are more salty than the lakes and rivers, and if their kidneys and gills were not constantly at work eliminating salt, they would absorb so much water that they might burst. Cartilaginous fishes form the only *isotonic* group – those whose internal salinity matches that outside, and who therefore have no need for regulatory mechanisms.

Whatever their differences of form and structure, few fishes are so startling as one netted in 1938. That was an exciting year for ichthyologists. Just before Christmas, a trawler working in the Mozambique Channel between Madagascar and Africa found an awesome creature in its catch. Steely blue, it was over five feet long and weighed 127 pounds. It was extraordinarily tough and took over three hours to die of suffocation, lunging and snapping at any crewmen who ventured close. Like the hagfish, it exuded quantities of mucus. Most remarkable, however, was the structure of its fins which, except for the spiny stabilizer in the centre of its back, were mounted on fleshy protuberances like truncated arms, each strengthened by bones. These have since earned the fish its nicknames of 'pawfish' and 'lobefin.'

No one on board the trawler had ever seen such a fish. Fortunately, the captain had the foresight to steam for the nearest port where ichthyologists could inspect his find. Out of the sea, as out of time itself, he had drawn a coelacanth, known to science until then only in fossils, and thought to have been extinct for 60 million years. It was a member of the crossopterygians (Greek: 'tassel-fins'), the ancestors of land vertebrates, and as a species it had existed virtually unchanged for 300 million years.

2 THE EVOLUTIONARY STRUGGLE

Despite its great antiquity, the coelacanth is still a highly developed vertebrate closely related to those fish that became amphibians. It tells biologists relatively little about the origins of fish – origins that are lost in an imperfect fossil record. For the last 600 million years the record of life is fairly complete, but when vertebrates appear in the record they are already highly developed, and stretching behind that appearance is a gulf of 100 million years.

Although the beginnings of vertebrate life are subjects of speculation, some present-day marine animals are probably very like the ancestors of fish. These are the protochordates, or lower chordates, organisms which combine vertebrate and invertebrate characteristics. The adult sea-squirt, for example, is a sedentary creature content to cling to a piling or a rock, siphoning food from the water and swaying with the current; but its tadpole state is remarkably well developed with a brain and a notochord, a flexible rod of linked cells, stretching through its long tail. In a sense, the sea-squirt degenerates as it grows, for the notochord gradually disappears and the nervous system withers. Eventually the sea-squirt shrouds itself, like a vegetable, in a sheath of material like cellulose.

More interesting is a two-inch protochordate called the lancelet, usually found on or near warm, sandy beaches. It is an unprepossessing creature. Although it has a liver, its digestive and respiratory systems generally resemble those of

The coelacanth

Until recently, Crossopterygians were believed to have been extinct since the days of the dinosaurs. When, in the 1930s, a coelacanth was caught in the Indian Ocean, and later examined by scientists, it was realized that at least one species, Latimeria chalumnae, had survived. This species is characterized by its lobed fins, tail tuft, its fat-filled pseudo-lung (or air bladder), a shark-like intestine with a spiral valve, and a hollow skeleton consisting of tubes of cartilage (the name 'coelacanth' means hollow spine). The coelacanth escaped notice for so long partly because it lives at great depths, from approximately 400 to 2,000 feet. Its flipper-like pectoral and pelvic fins are fore-runners of the limbs used by closely related fish which gave rise to amphibians and reptiles. The coelacanth is truly a living fossil, for it has changed very little in 300 million years. The early stage of development displayed by their internal organs has provided interesting evidence of the evolution of vertebrates.

19

Evidence from the past

One of the most interesting items that can be learned from fossils is the extent to which the seas once covered the land area of North America. The marine herring fossil, Diplomystus (left), was unearthed in Green River, Wyoming – one of the most fertile sources of fossil fish on the continent. Canada is not without fossil remains, however. A Royal Ontario Museum expedition (right) on the Horsefly River, British Columbia, collected fish fossils from the shale of the region by splitting the rock along the thin laminations. The specimens were later studied in the laboratory and their geological ages established. The salmon tail fossil (below) found at Smithers, British Columbia, is believed to be the oldest salmon tail fossil in existence – being dated at 50 million years old. The sucker head fossil (below right) from the Horsefly River expedition is noteworthy since it displays a terminal mouth – an early stage of development before the true sucker mouth evolved.

21

lower animals. It has no heart – its blood being circulated by rhythmic contractions of the vessels – but it does have a main ventral blood chamber, and the veins returning from the gills form themselves into a dorsal aorta, an arrangement very similar to that found in fishes. Most important, the lancelet has a notochord which it retains through life and which, during its embryonic stage, rises from deeper in its body to meet the dorsal nerve. This pattern is followed in the development of all true vertebrates.

The lancelet is too specialized to be a direct ancestor of fishes, but somewhere in the warm Palaeozoic seas a similar creature made the internal adjustments that eventually led to the evolution of fishes and hence of all other vertebrates.

Intact fish fossils have been found in rocks made 420 million years ago. These were the ostracoderms, the bony-skins. These heavily armoured, jawless bottom-dwellers had only one pair of undeveloped fins and sucking mouths not unlike a sturgeon's. Their internal skeletons were cartilaginous and their backbones extended to the end of the tail, as they do in sharks. Each of their gills seems to have been contained in a separate pouch of muscle, so that breathing likely consisted of the synchronized expansion and contraction of these muscles. Ostracoderms averaged about two feet in length. Obviously they represented a tremendous advance over organisms such as the lancelet; however, by the end of the Devonian Period, about 350 million years ago, they had joined all other agnathans, except lampreys and hagfish, in extinction. Quicker and more flexible types had evolved and triumphed in the struggle for food and habitat. What proved decisive in that struggle were two characteristics displayed by the placoderm, the ostracoderm's successor: jaws and paired fins.

Other animals had grown plates around their mouths, and these functioned as weak jaws, but true jaws evolved from the foremost gill arch. This advance can scarcely be overestimated, for it was at least as important as the later development of amphibians' legs. It meant that fish were no longer confined to the bottom where they sucked up their food like animated vacuum cleaners. Now they could snip off vegetation, seize small prey, and even crack open previously safe crustaceans. Over the millions of years during which jaws

Scales, jaws, fins, tails

Fishes were the pioneers in the development of many characteristics besides the internal skeleton. Their protective scales (below) gave them protection without the inflexibility of a solid external armour. Jaws in fish range in function from vacuum cleaners (sturgeon) to rapacious, tooth-filled clamps (shark).

The common shiner illustrates the most familiar arrangement of fins. The sculpins, of which the red Irish lord is an example, have heavily armed dorsal spines in one of the two dorsal fins and fan-shaped pectorals on which they rest. The brightly coloured dorsal fin of the grayling is used for courting and fighting displays.

The tails of fishes serve primarily as a means of propulsion, but the flounder uses its tail only rarely, whereas the salmon, tuna and mackerel, which have heavily muscled tails, are famous for their long migrations. The sharp-like, heterocercal tail of sturgeon is typical of fish denser than water.

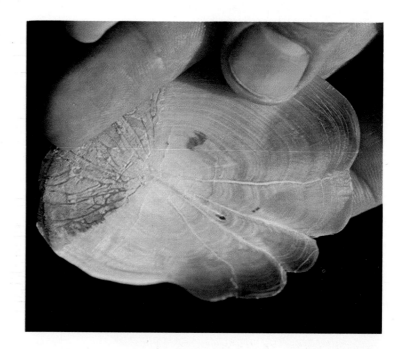

ABOVE: *SHARK* BELOW: *COMMON SHINER*　　　ABOVE: *STURGEON* BELOW: *SCULPIN*　　　ABOVE: *SALMON* BELOW: *GRAYLING*

OW: *FLOUNDER*　　　BELOW: *SALMON*　　　BELOW: *STURGEON*

ABOVE: *PERCH* BELOW: *ROCKFISH*

ABOVE: *FLOUNDER* BELOW: *GREENLING*

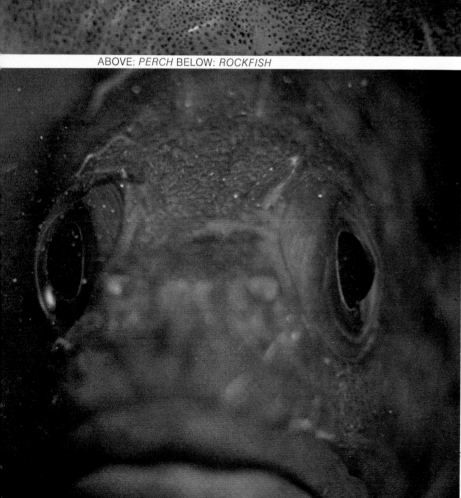

grew, strengthened, and developed specialized teeth and muscles, the fish possessing them enjoyed a favoured position.

The ability to seize smaller fish, for example, was a marked advantage, but capture required pursuit, and pursuit required speed. During their reign, placoderms experimented with various forms of locomotive and steering devices. One armour-plated fellow, the antiarch, developed segmented legs similar to a lobster's. But this, of course, was basically another modification for life on the seabed. Once they had left the security of the bottom, fish required not only a strengthened tail for propulsion, but also some means of stabilizing themselves so that they would not pitch helplessly and roll in cross currents. Fins were the answer. Precisely how they evolved is unknown, but probably they developed from skin folds between protective spines and the body. In time, the value of these extra flaps led to their further refinement.

Differences in fin structure might have given bony fishes an evolutionary edge. Their fins are more flexible than those of cartilaginous types, and the greater mobility they provided probably helped them to adapt to ecological niches beyond reach of sharks and rays. In any case, 150 million years ago the Osteichthyes began to proliferate, and their numbers have expanded ever since. They have become by far the most adaptable of classes.

---

3 MODIFICATIONS FOR MOVEMENT

The principal fact governing fish movement is that water is incompressible and about 800 times denser than air. A fish must therefore advance by pushing water aside. Its characteristic motion is a rhythmic undulation which begins with the back-and-forth sweep of its streamlined head and ends with its tail fin, a rhythm duplicated by both amphibians

Fishes' vision is limited by the low levels of light in the water and by the fact that images diffuse quickly with distance. Most fishes, however, have the advantages of a wide field of vision.

and reptiles. The method is extremely effective. Dolphins frequently reach thirty-seven miles per hour, and flying fish take off at about the same velocity. Blue marlins can maintain a cruising rate of nearly fifty miles per hour, and barracudas are thought to go over sixty in short bursts.

The caudal fin, the primary driving force, may be one of two shapes. In sharks and sturgeons, the spinal column extends to the tip of the tail, leaving the smaller bottom lobe to be supported by cartilaginous rays. This *heterocercal* pattern reaches an extreme modification in thresher sharks; these fish hunt in packs, using the elongated upper lobes of their tails to herd the prey before attacking. Most bony fishes have what is known as a *homocercal* tail, in which bony rays fan out more or less symmetrically from the end of the spine, forming two matched lobes.

On the fish's back are one or two dorsal fins, and underneath is the anal fin. Set closer to the head, two pairs of smaller fins may be used for steering, balance, propulsion, or all three. These are the pectorals (corresponding to the arms of higher vertebrates), usually located just behind the gills, and the pelvics (corresponding to the legs), situated near and under the pectorals in bony fishes, and farther back in cartilaginous species. All are controlled by overlapping blocks of muscles, called *myotomes*, which are linked to the framework of the skeleton.

Of course, many fishes have modified their fins just as they have modified their body shapes. Seahorses have a prehensile tail instead of a caudal fin, and the disc-like ocean sunfish has a ruffle around its rump. The common eel has a continuous fin which runs down its back, around the end of its body, and up the belly. The clingfish has modified its pectoral and pelvic fins into an effective suction cup which it uses to hold onto rocks, and the remora has done the same thing with its front dorsal fin, using the suction cup on its head to hitchhike on the bellies of sharks. Part of the deep-sea angler's front dorsal fin is used like a fishing pole, dangling a lure over the waiting mouth. Rays have simplified their tail into whip-like appendages, while at the same time extending their pectoral fins into great wings which are actually capable of lifting them out of the water and through the air. The male swordtail's anal fin serves as a sexual organ. Finally, some fish have dispensed with some fins altogether.

Varied as their shapes and functions are, fins are spiny and membranous extensions of the fish's body covering. It is true that some spines are anchored so deeply in the muscles that they may actually be considered part of the skeleton, and that the lobes of the coelacanth's fins are supported by skeletal extensions like rudimentary arms and legs; but the interconnecting membranes between spines and fin rays are part of the fish's outer covering, or dermis.

In most mature fish the dermis is covered by scales – overlapping wafers set in individual pockets, which grow as the fish grows. In some types, like the boxfish, the scales have thickened and fused into an effective exoskeleton, while in eels they are so deeply embedded in the skin that they seem non-existent. In lampreys and catfish they are absent; and in such species as the globefish or the pufferfish, they have become elongated and sharpened into protective spines. Basically, however, scales come in four types. Most distinctive are the keen, tooth-like *placoid* scales of the shark. Primitive bony fishes, such as paddlefishes, garpikes, and sturgeons, are covered with small, squarish plates – *ganoid* scales, which give the fish a polished appearance. The most common scales, however, are the *ctenoid* (rough with a comb-like edge) and the smoother, often circular, *cycloid* variety. Both of these latter types permit greater freedom of movement than the heavier ganoid scales of the sturgeon, and some highly developed species have both types.

Around and under the scales are various kinds of glands. Mucous glands are especially abundant in lampreys, hagfish, and sharks, but most fish are generously supplied with them. The slime they secrete lubricates and heals the skin, as well as helping to protect it against infestation from parasites. A few fishes secrete poison from special skin glands, and many species use colour glands in the skin to change their hue as required. This transformation is accomplished by shifts in two types of cells: the chromatophores and the iridocytes. Chromatophores are cells containing red, orange, yellow, and black granules which can concentrate or disperse as required, thus either intensifying or lightening their respective colours. Iridocytes are actually grains of a waste product called *guanine* which cannot be excreted through fishes' kidneys and

so ends up, together with lime, on the skin. Iridocytes reflect colours and give the fish its white or silvery sheen.

Photophores, tiny cellular 'flashlights' embedded in the skin, are unknown among freshwater species but fairly common in sea-going types, especially those dwelling below 1,500 feet. Here, all is darkness except for whatever light is made by hatchet fish, lanternfish, black swallowers, and others as they send messages, lure prey, and defend themselves by sudden flashes of brilliance. These lights are produced in two ways: either by a chemical and nervous reaction in the photophores, or by luminous bacteria that live symbiotically in pore-like openings in their host's skin.

Perhaps the most interesting of all the fish's specialized skin glands and sensors are those that form the lateral line. This line is a string of pressure-sensitive cells (neuromasts) set in pores and joined by a nerve running just beneath the skin. One such line stretches back from the fish's head on each side, linked to sensory equipment on the skull. Frequently it runs the whole length of the body. On most Canadian game fish it is clearly distinguishable as a slight discoloration. Although not completely understood, its function seems to be to detect subtle changes of pressure and current, warning of approaching danger, aiding navigation in murky water, and enabling schools of fish to hold formation like a single organism. It functions, in fact, like a delicate sixth sense.

---

4 REFINEMENT OF SENSES

In sharks and rays, the lateral line system is responsive to temperature changes as well as to pressure, but in bony fishes temperature is sensed through nerve endings distributed over the skin. These nerves, particularly numerous in the head, are also sensitive to touch, and some fish have extended them by growing long feelers, or barbels, on their snouts. The 'whiskers' of the catfish, a resident of murky water, are perhaps the most familiar of these, but the most ancient and lordly of all Canada's freshwater fishes also possesses them.

The sturgeon is a bottom-dweller, preferring the sandy

Distinctive features

The lateral line (below), an organ seen clearly on this trout, functions primarily to sense vibrations, such as pressure and current changes. More unusual modifications are seen in the *porcupine fish* (left) *and the midshipman* (above). *The scales of the porcupine fish have developed into elongated, protective spines. Photophores are used to illuminate the environment by some fish, but in the bottom-dwelling midshipman, the line of photophores is used as a lighted signalling device.*

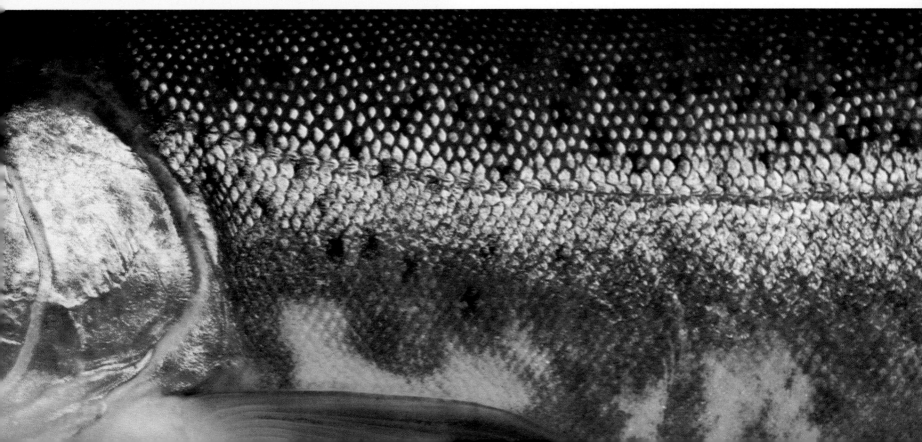

plains of cold northern lakes. Its mouth is located underneath and toward the back of its head. As it feeds – sucking up small crustaceans, insect larvae, and fish – it tilts its jaws downward and forward for more efficient operation. Because it cannot always see the potential prey it has barbels equipped with both nerves and taste buds. There are four of these barbels, crossing like a sparse moustache midway between the sturgeon's snout tip and mouth.

The sturgeon's method of feeding may not be as elegant or as quick as that of some other species, but it has been remarkably successful. Fish never stop growing, although the rate of growth slows with age, and sturgeon have attained by far the largest size among the fishes of Canada's lakes. They do not even reach maturity until they are twenty years old. Early Canadian snapshots often show lines of eight or ten men holding a seven-foot, 300-pound sturgeon. Nor are the Canadian sturgeons the largest on record. The beluga, famous for Caspian caviar, often weighs more than a ton; the biggest ever caught was twenty-eight feet, 2,860 pounds.

Sturgeons are not the only fish to have exterior taste buds. Many species have evolved them on their lips, snouts, chin barbels, heads, bodies, and even tails, so that dubious food may be sampled before it is gulped down. Some have even modified fins for tasting.

Taste and smell are, therefore, much less closely related in fishes than they are in mammals. Like most mammals, however, fishes have an extremely keen sense of smell, which they probably rely on more than any other sense. Their forebrain is mainly concerned with smell. In sharks and other predators, this portion of the brain is especially large. Skindivers know that any speared and bleeding fish must be quickly taken out of the water, for sharks can scent blood from extreme distances and it is irresistible to them; often they will even tear at each other in the frenzy of feeding. Some fish can detect repugnant substances even when they are diluted in two million parts of water; eels can detect some scents in one million, million, million parts of water! Once the fish's remarkable sense of smell is appreciated, the migrations of anadromous species, such as salmon, become less mysterious if no less amazing. Biologists now think that, after spending most of their lives at sea, they literally smell their way home guided

The barbels of catfish (opposite) *and sturgeon* (above) *function as sense organs, although only the sturgeon has taste buds on its barbels. The sturgeon samples the taste of an object with its 'whiskers,' lowers its protrusible mouth in an elevator action, and sucks the food up. The action is demonstrated here.*

by an ancient memory and by minute quantities of water from the pools where they were born.

The physical apparatus that makes possible such a feat seems simple. Two nostrils, or nares, open from the fish's snout into a chamber lined with olfactory sensors. As water flows over and around these sensors, the brain analyzes the messages it receives. The nares have nothing to do with breathing; in fact, in all but a few species, the sac to which they lead is a dead end. In sharks, both nares must be open for the sense of smell to function properly. When researchers plugged one hole in an experiment with a shark, the fish could not 'home in' on the source of an attractive smell, and instead swam helplessly in circles. It is tempting to speculate that the spaced nares give perspective on an odour in much the same way that binocular vision allows a perception of depth.

Most bony fishes are myopic, but some have refined their sight in remarkable ways. The trout, for example, can use different areas of its retina to focus simultaneously on separate objects, one near and one distant – a trick permitted by the elliptical shape of its lens. Predators such as the northern pike have a sighting groove running from each eye toward the tip of the snout, apparently as an aid to binocular vision. The *cuatro ojos*, or foureyes, of Central and South America hunts with the surface of the water cutting through the middle of each eye, alert for both airborne and aquatic prey. Separate retinas allow this refinement, and a specially shaped lens compensates for refraction. The best vision of all is probably enjoyed by benthic species. Since they communicate and hunt by means of lights, they must always be watchful for even the smallest glimmer in the darkness. Vivid coloration and the ability to perceive it is useful only to the inhabitants of shallow waters, for all the lighter colours of the spectrum tend to be filtered out in the first few fathoms, leaving the deeper regions blends of dark blue and green.

As we have seen, the lights of deep-sea fish are made either by photophores or bacterial hitchhikers, not by electricity. However, electricity is a unique part of the sensory equipment of many fish species. It has a double function: first, it is an effective weapon; second, it is an extension of the sense of touch. Fish, such as the electric eel, the torpedo ray, and the electric catfish, that have some muscles modified for the generation of electricity may use it both ways, although the second use usually requires a drastic reduction in voltage. The electrical eel, for example, can generate a charge of 650 volts at one amp, although it rarely looses a maximum shock, preferring to eat prey that has been stunned, not killed. For navigational purposes in murky waters, however, the eel surrounds itself with a field of low voltage (positive at front, negative at rear) which functions like radar. Incoming signals are received by sensors on the head. Electric eels become increasingly dependent on this radar, for although they grow to at least eight feet, from the time they are a foot long their eyes begin to degenerate and they eventually become

blind. Receptors dot the entire body of another electrical fish, the African mormyroid, which has the distinction of owning the largest cerebellum, relative to body size, of any vertebrate.

Fish have no external ears, and it was long thought that they were incapable of talking to each other, or even of hearing. However, they do have an inner ear, a complex of tiny canals and fine bones, which is perfectly capable of hearing in the ordinary sense, although its range seems to be restricted to quite low frequencies – around 250 cycles per second. These vibrations may be received either by the lateral line or by the bony structure of the whole fish. In some cases, the vibrations are amplified by the air bladder. Carp, whose air bladders are directly connected to the ear, have very acute hearing.

The air bladder is also used to make sound. Some fishes simply expel air from it in grunting noises, but others utilize its value as a resonating chamber. These either vibrate the muscles of its walls (much like beating a drum) or rub together bones that lie close to it. Mackerel also communicate by grinding teeth located in the throat.

Part of the inner ear structure is the statocyst, a chamber lined with sensory hairs, filled with fluid, and containing either a grain of sand or an 'ear stone' of calcium. This is the fish's organ of balance, controlling, via the brain, the movement of the stabilizing pectoral and pelvic fins, and the flow of gas to and from the air bladder.

---

5 GILLS AND LUNGS

Normal respiration occurs through the gills, delicate but highly capable breathing mechanisms. In fact, gills are far more efficient than human lungs; they extract about 80 per cent of the oxygen from the water which flows over them, whereas the human lung removes only 25 per cent of the oxygen from the air it breathes. In general, sea water is more highly aerated than fresh water, streams contain more oxygen than lakes, and lakes are richer breathing zones than are ponds. The changes in the breathing apparatus which led first to the air bladder (also called a gas, swim, or flotation

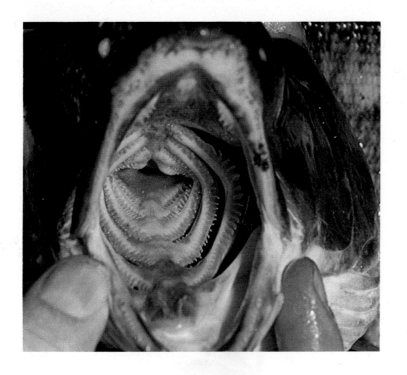

bladder) and then to lungs probably were made first by fishes who found themselves in stagnating water. What occurred is suggested by such species as goldfish, which can supplement their oxygen supply with air held in the gullet. In time, that portion of the gullet used as a reservoir would tend to stretch upwards, enlarging into an elongated pocket and eventually into a rudimentary lung. Primitive species like the bowfin and the garpike still have their air bladders connected to the oesophagus or gut, but in most bony fishes the air bladder performs no respiratory function. It lies separated from other organs in the centre of the fish just under the spine. Lampreys, hagfish, sharks, and other fishes which are believed to have evolved in the ocean have no air bladders, and the coelacanth's is filled with fat.

Water taken through the fish's mouth passes over the gill rakers, which strain out the food, and then passes over the gill filaments, which take in oxygen and give up carbon dioxide.

The internal organs of the fish are well suited to its aquatic environment. The air bladder, a hydrostatic organ which appears to have developed from a primitive lung in early fishes, has no respiratory function in bony fishes.

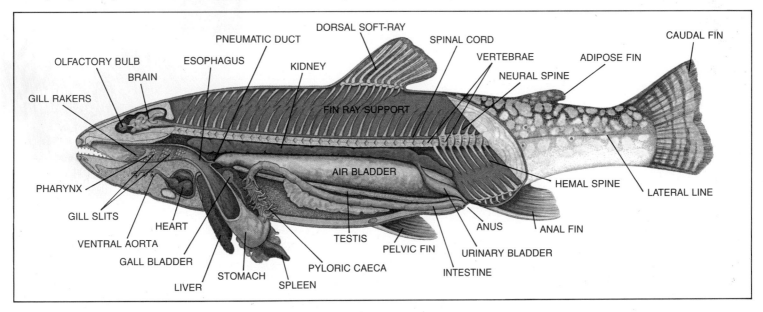

Mass die-offs of alewives (an ill-adapted oceanic intruder) occur in the Great Lakes when these fish migrate to the shallow waters to spawn, or at other times of stress.

The function of the air bladder in most fish is buoyancy control. It acts like a small balloon. By increasing the amount of gas in its bladder, a fish can rise without moving a muscle, and by ejecting gas it can sink. When the hydrostatic balance is exact, the fish can rest, but species such as the mackerel in which the air bladder is either miniscule or absent, must swim constantly. The gas (usually oxygen, sometimes nitrogen) is transported to and from the bladder by the blood. Changes are therefore made very slowly. If a fish is hauled up too quickly from the depths, the gas in its air bladder will expand as the external pressure lessens, exploding it.

With the modification of gills and air bladders into air-breathing apparatuses, about 350 million years ago, fishes began to transcend their generic limitations and to evolve into amphibians. A new, marshy world spread before them. The first explorers were probably not unlike several living species – eels, which use mucus to absorb oxygen from the air; mudskippers, with specialized gill chambers; loaches, whose intestines can absorb swallowed oxygen; and lungfish, which can survive for months wrapped in dried balls of mud. All of these air-breathing fishes can pull themselves along on land by their pectoral fins. The main stock of amphibian life, however, probably grew from adventuring crossopterygians, like the tough and ancient coelacanth.

standing, they are not safe from our assaults. In theory, overfishing is impossible, since fishing ceases to be profitable before the nucleus of a breeding stock is destroyed. In fact, overfishing has already eliminated the lake sturgeon from U.S. waters and made it a rarity through much of its Canadian range. The regal white sturgeon of British Columbia is similarly threatened, as are the Atlantic sturgeon, the Atlantic salmon, the shad, and at least two dozen other North American fishes. Even if fishermen leave what they consider to be an adequate breeding stock, they have no control over natural vagaries such as disease, freak predation, or sudden temperature changes which could carry off the remaining members of a species. Man's dams and pollution tend to make such events more likely, for they reduce the diversity of life in the waters, and as a habitat grows simpler it grows less stable. The poisoning of the seas from which life emerged is an almost unthinkable prospect; and yet, in a period which is scarcely a flicker of geological time, our industries and cities have ruined some waterways and debased countless others. No one can predict how serious our cumulative chemical assault on the oceans will be. Reductions in the earth's oxygen supply and radical changes in climate are not beyond possibility.

The next time we see a fish belly-up in a polluted stream, we would do well to recall what brought it there – 500 million years of evolution and a few decades of human arrogance. Under the circumstances, the old Tsimshian tale of juvenile wantonness takes on new meaning; it seems less like quaint folklore, more like a warning.

WAYLAND DREW

6 MAN'S ASSAULTS

The fishes' journey has been long – at least 500 million years from the first aquatic vertebrates to the present. Nor is it finished yet. The sea remains mysterious. Man knows far from everything about its inhabitants, and about their place in the balances of the planet.

Unfortunately, although they may lie beyond our under-

Ancestral ways

Fish have always played an important part in the diet of coastal Indians, although with the encroachment of white man's civilization over the years, this dependence has diminished.

In British Columbia, special provisions are made to allow Indians to catch salmon in rivers during spawning periods, using other methods than sports fishermen are allowed to use. Thus, they can use a variety of equipment, including nets, traps and spears.

These special privileges apply only to fish that Indians catch for their own consumption. To avoid the illegal sale of these fish, Indians are required to identify them with a special mark as soon as they are removed from the water. If they neglect to do so, they are liable for prosecution.

The man (right) has had a successful afternoon of fishing and is in the process of cleaning his catch.

34

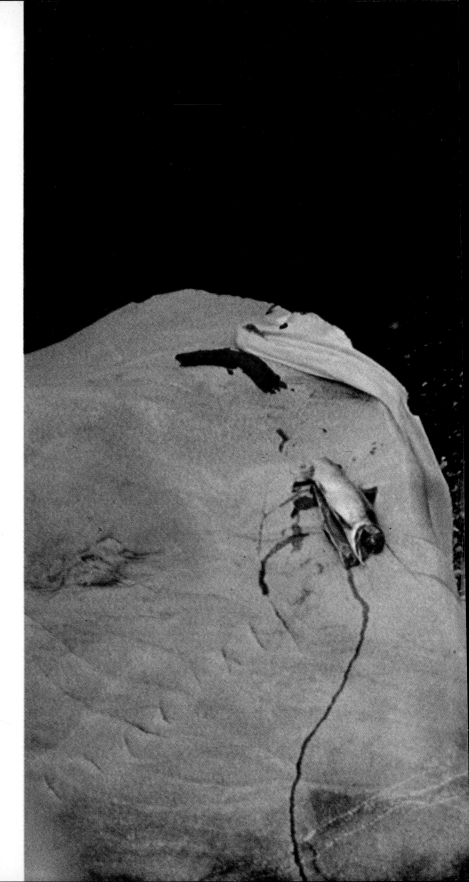

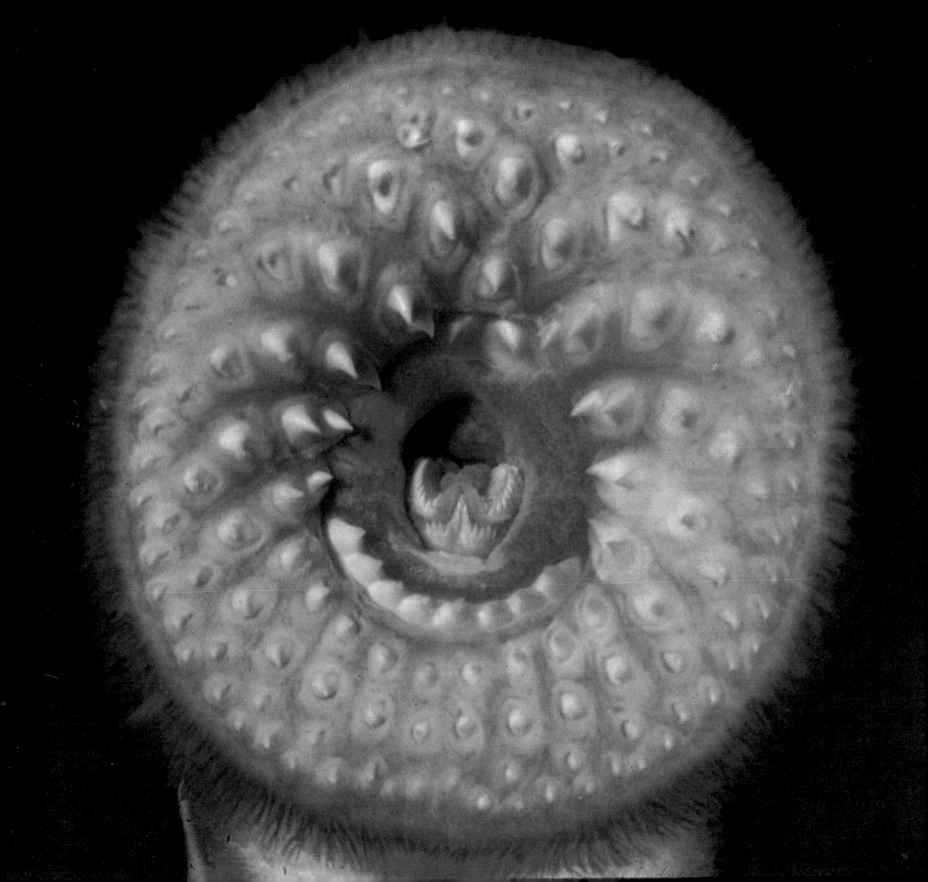

PART TWO
THE FIRST VERTEBRATES

Fishes are the earth's oldest vertebrates, the group from which all higher forms of life emerged. Their history goes back nearly half a billion years. During the Devonian period (405 to 345 million years ago), fishes diversified and evolved to fill both the oceans and fresh waters with specialists in almost every imaginable underwater way of life. Fossils of large-toothed predators have been found along with their smaller prey. Jawless parasitic fishes existed upon the living flesh and blood of their scaly kin, while schools of gentle, bottom-feeding fishes sifted quietly through sunlit, muddy bottoms. Most forms known from these early fossils are now extinct, although we can recognize some existing species as their obvious descendants. Some few, however, remain today essentially unchanged, living now, as they did so long ago, their simple lives.

The parasitic lamprey fastens itself to its victims by means of its disc-like mouth. The rasp-like teeth on the tongue penetrate through the scales and into the flesh. Many fish die from a lamprey attack, although larger ones may survive.

The class Pisces now contains many more species than all other classes of vertebrates put together. There are something in the order of 20,000 species swimming, wriggling, or just floating throughout the oceans, lakes, rivers, creeks, and ponds which cover three-quarters of the earth. And more are being discovered.

If fishes came into their own during the Devonian Period, laying down the basis for modern fishy forms and social structures, we must consider what went before and from where (or rather whom) they derived their beginnings.

7 INCREASING FLEXIBILITY

The great division of the animal kingdom lies between the vertebrates and the invertebrates. Science has focused upon the possession of vertebrae and other related characteristics as the major dividing line between higher and lower animals. Most animals are invertebrates. Vertebrates, in spite of all the honour and prominence they are accorded, represent only one phylum of the animal kingdom; whereas invertebrates occupy about twenty-five phyla of widely differing animals. The invertebrates not only established the base from which the higher forms – starting with the fishes – evolved, they also provide the broad-based foundation upon which all food or energy dependencies function. The vertebrates – including man – have never lost their dependence upon these lowlier forms.

At the top of the invertebrate evolutionary tree, and representing millions of years of evolution, are the protochordates, living a rather passive way of life on or near the ocean's floor. They are remarkable because they evolved a rod, made up of turgid cells, as an internal support for their bodies. This rod, or *notochord*, is seen as the precursor to the spinal column of the first fishes. The possession of it gave some unknown protochordate the potential to become the ancestor of all the vertebrates.

Up to this point, all animals had been soft-bodied or had possessed a hard, shell-like exoskeleton akin to that of modern crabs and lobsters. The development of the internal skeleton (endoskeleton), be it of cartilage or bone, had the advantage of giving fishes the great flexibility of movement that is so necessary to their active way of life. Furthermore, their growth could progress steadily with their daily survival activities unimpaired. Invertebrates possessing an exoskeleton cannot grow inside its confinement and must hide themselves from their predators and fast while they shed the old 'shell,' put on a growth-spurt, then excrete and harden the new one.

The endoskeleton provides a firm anchor for fishes' powerful swimming muscles as well as a support and protection for their internal organs. Up to this point, animals had been limited in size, but with this skeletal innovation (as mechanically sound in large animals as it is in small ones), fishes could begin to increase in bulk and size.

The earliest vertebrates were strange-looking creatures. They were somewhat fish-like, but had no jaws or fins. Their evolving skeletons were more cartilaginous than bony, and contained passages for their nervous system.

The pre-vertebrate evolutionary story took place in the Precambrian period prior to the start of the Palaeozoic era. The first organisms, being soft-bodied, have left few fossils. Our attempts to understand the origin of fishes must rest upon indirect evidence and shrewd scientific guesswork. Evolutionary relationships, learned from later groups which have provided ample evidence both living, dead, and fossilized, have been projected *backwards* to suggest what has gone before. Similarities in patterns of development and biochemical homologies (similarities of structure suggesting common ancestry) in living forms have also provided the basis for the scientific speculations. The story as it is told today does not satisfy all educated opinion, for there are differing views on many of the essentials. However, as new knowledge becomes available from the efforts of a growing corps of scientists, present theories are constantly being revised, deletions and additions made, and the evolutionary process is becoming better understood.

---

8 TOWARDS MORE VARIETY

During the past 500 million years, there has been a tendency for some organisms to leave the oceans to adapt to progressively less-congenial surroundings in fresh water and upon the land. We may safely assume they did so in response to overcrowding and competition in the oceans. Long-term climatic changes tended to create new environments, and new environments presented fresh opportunities for food and living space.

The transition from the sea to fresh water might appear no great evolutionary step for both are aquatic environments. There are, however, fundamental problems to be solved be-

Dinichthys, *the 'terrible fish,' was common in the Devonian period. It grew to thirty feet in length, and was partially covered by a hinged sheath of armour. This fish, shown here preying on a primitive shark, was a placoderm, an early jawed vertebrate.*

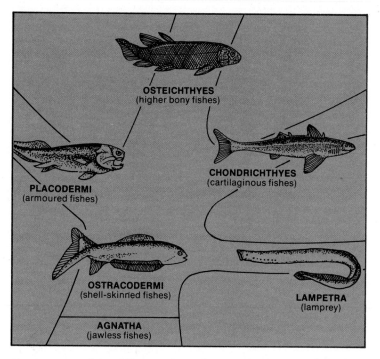

Lampreys and hagfish are the only representatives of the first class of fishes, Agnatha, to survive. The other major classes evolved as shown here: Placodermi, the extinct armoured fishes; Chondrichthyes, the cartilaginous fishes; and Osteichthyes, the bony fishes.

A 'preadaptation' is defined as any fortuitous characteristic an animal owns that allows it to adapt readily to a new way of life. The arthropods had heavy but 'streamlined' bodies and jointed legs with which to crawl along the bottom; the fish also had streamlined bodies as well as their flexible internal skeletons and the ability to swim, at least sluggishly. Both kinds initially subsisted by a grubbing, bottom-sifting way of life.

The first Ordovician fish were of the class Agnatha (jawless fishes). As well as their primitive mouth parts, they had heavy, shell-like skins composed of large, tough scales. They were small in size and were poor swimmers. They expanded their numbers throughout the Silurian period (which lasted for 20 million years) and on to a peak in the early Devonian, but then they declined rapidly, to disappear early in the Mississippian leaving only a couple of species – the lampreys and hagfish—to survive until today. They doubtless lost out to the placoderms (the class Placodermi), which appeared some 50 million years after the advent of the agnathans and became the first vertebrates with jaws.

Whereas the agnathans had been limited to filtering through the benthic ooze for the sedentary organisms that made up their diets, the placoderms, by evolving the first jaws, freed themselves from this somewhat limited and competitive way of life. With jaws, prey could be sought and grasped at any depth. The stronger the jaws and bigger the mouth, the larger the prey that could be pursued. It was not long before the first teeth made their appearance.

The placoderms took the predatory way a step further by evolving paired fins and greater size. The increased control and coordination that came with the paired fins allowed a variety of hunting techniques to develop. Placoderms ranged in size from small, swiftly swimming forms to large bottom-dwellers who struck from ambush. Jaw fragments found near Exshaw, Alberta, are estimated to have come from a placoderm thirty feet in length. As their name implied, all placoderms possessed body armour.

Just as an early agnathan had given rise to the placoderms in the Ordivician, the placoderms gave rise in the Devonian to two more advanced classes of freshwater fishes – each destined to replace its armoured ancestor. These were the

fore an organism can survive the change. In order to live in fresh water, an oceanic species must develop special mechanisms in order to avoid gaining too much fresh water by osmosis. Modern anadromous fishes, like the salmon, which live part of their life cycle in the oceans and part in fresh waters, must adapt not just once in their evolutionary history, but as often as they run up into the rivers to spawn.

The fresh waters were invaded first by plants and invertebrate sea animals. They were followed by higher predators. First came the arthropods and, in the late Ordivician, the early vertebrate fishes. In order to adapt to life further and further upstream, these pioneers had to cope with swift currents not encountered in the oceans. Fishes and arthropods both had preadaptations that aided their escape from the seas.

Chondrichthyes – fishes with cartilaginous skeletons including all modern sharks, skates, sawfishes, and rays – and the Osteichthyes or bony fishes.

The sharks left fresh water to invade the seas towards the end of the Devonian, ahead of the bony fishes, and became the oceans' greatest group of predators. Changing comparatively little down through the years, they still possess cartilaginous skeletons. A few species have reinvaded fresh water. The bony fishes, however, were to become the more prominent class.

By the middle of the Devonian, bony fishes were already dominant in fresh water – dominating even the sharks. All initially possessed rudimentary lungs, doubtless as a survival measure against droughts, but these gave way to air bladders when the class followed the sharks into the stability of the oceans and began an acceleration of their evolution. The oceans have been properly described as the cradle of life. We must now recognize that, for vertebrate life at least, fresh-water streams and lakes were for a time its nursery.

The viperfish, one of the luminescent fishes living in the ocean deeps, has such long, needle-like teeth that they remain outside the mouth when it is closed.

9 THE DOMINANT ORDER

During the Devonian, the most common bony fishes by far were the lobefins of the subclass Crossopterygii. They were aggressive predators, armed with strong jaws and possessing some structural features that suggest they were ancestral to the amphibians. An offshoot branch of the crossopterygians developed later in Mesozoic seas into the stub-nosed, weak-jawed coelacanths. It was thought that this branch of the crossopterygians had become extinct along with the dinosaurs. In 1938, the discovery of the first of a series of fresh-caught, four-to-five-foot specimens from South African seas and the deep waters off the Comores Islands in the Indian Ocean proved that one species, *latimeria chalumnae*, had survived. Since its discovery, it has been eagerly collected, dissected, and photographed – in order to compare its flesh-and-blood realities with the fossilized impressions of its ancestors.

The earliest bony fishes are divided into two subclasses – the Sarcopterygii and Actinopterygii. The Sarcopterygii are in the direct line of descent for the higher animals and man. They contain the dipnoans (ancestors of modern lungfish) and are therefore our very distant cousins, possessing characteristics ancient and curious. Of the lungfishes (Dipnoi), three genera still survive, one each in the tropical regions of Australia, Africa, and South America. There is a definite resemblance between the long-bodied lungfishes and some lizard-like early amphibians. The lungfish's ability to survive droughts and the complete drying-up of water by burrowing into the mud and by estivating has led earlier researchers to label them the ancestors of the prototype amphibian. Estivation – a process akin to hibernation except that it is used to survive heat and the lack of water rather than cold – is common to the South American and African forms. The Australian species survives in what stagnant water remains by gulping air at the surface. It now appears that the related crossop-

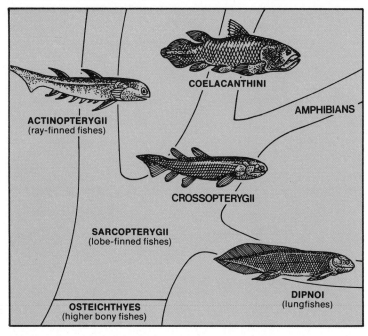

Bony fishes are divided into two groups: Actinopterygii, ray-finned fishes; and Sarcopterygii, fleshy-finned fishes, from which developed amphibians, an evolutionary pathway to mankind.

terygians previously mentioned also had species capable of such feats as well as a fin arrangement better preadapted to form the basis of terrestrial legs. Some authorities believe that the crossopterygians themselves may have occasionally crawled overland in search of water on their 'lobed' fins, conveniently located on stumpy limb-like projections.

Common during the Devonian, today's lungfishes have all survived in areas characterized by regular seasonal dry-ups. There, they can still exploit their curious adaptation by emerging at the start of the wet season to enjoy life relatively free from fishy competition. Theirs is a very specialized little niche. One estivating specimen was dug up from the bed of a dried-up African pond, wrapped in brown paper, tied with string, labelled, and despatched by sea to London. After weeks en route it arrived looking like a dessicated piece of old

leather and was dunked into an aquarium. Within half a day, it had resumed its proper appearance and proportions and was swimming hungrily around the tank. Its dependence upon oxygen acquired in this un-fishy mode of mouth-breathing is such that if held underwater too long it will drown.

The Actinopterygii (ray-finned fishes) were, from Devonian times on, the main group of fishes. Their principal characteristic is their fins, composed of a web of skin supported by spines or soft rays. Rayfins had large eyes, which doubtless contributed to their evolutionary success over the sarcopterygians, who depended largely upon the sense of smell for their awareness of their surroundings and the presence of food. In the ray-finned group, the olfactory organs are present but are small and unimportant. Their eyes are large and their brains organized to favour sight, which was clearly their principal sensory tool. For fishes whose descendants would tend increasingly to hunt their food in the clear, open waters of the oceans, this new development was of great potential survival value.

Changes in their manner of breathing may also have played a part in their success story, for this group alone accomplished the transformation from the lung to the air bladder. A fish's air or swim bladder is a hydrostatic organ used to determine the fish's buoyancy and the depth at which it swims. Here again is an adaptation of considerable future potential to a group of animals spreading out into the oceans. Perhaps more important than even the development of fin, eye, or air bladder was the change in reproductive emphasis that the actinopterygians accomplished. Hitherto, fishes had laid relatively few eggs to ensure the continuance of each species; perhaps a few dozens or even a few hundreds. Sarcopterygians had laid large eggs, which although few in number, were abundantly supplied with yolk. The rayfins, on the other hand, laid much smaller and more numerous eggs. Thousands or even millions were laid each spawning season

Gars have unusual scales, attached to each other by joints. So hard are these scales, it is claimed that they were once used by Indians as arrowheads.

CLADOSELACHE

DINICHTHYS

BOTHRIOLEPIS

The Devonian period—the age of fishes

OSTEOLEPIS

DIPTERUS

CHEIROLEPIS

CLIMATIUS

CEPHALASPIS

VLASTA VAN KAMPEN

The Devonian seas were populated with placoderms like the enormous Dinichthys. Sharks and bony fishes also appeared in the Devonian period and quickly became dominant in the fresh waters and, not much later, in the seas.

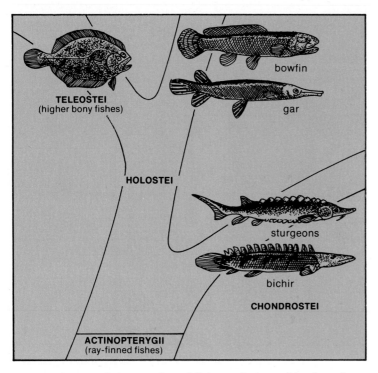

The evolution of the ray-finned fishes culminated in the teleost. Although most living ray-fins are teleosts, there are survivors, like the sturgeon and bowfin, of the older groups.

by a single female. Most would be lost to predators and scavengers. Enough, however, remained to ensure not only the survival of this group but also its ascendancy. Their numbers increased dramatically.

The rayfins divided into three superorders. The first, *Chondrostei*, were represented in the Palaeozoic by numerous genera of small, shiny-scaled fishes called palaeoniscids with heterocercal (shark-like) tails. However, the numbers of individuals they represented in total was not great, and they tended to be outnumbered and overshadowed by the lobe-finned fishes and lungfishes of their day. The *Chondrostei* survive today only in the forms of the sturgeons of Eurasia and North America, the paddlefish of the Mississippi, and the bichir of the Nile. All are atypical, for most of the ancestral characteristics have become modified, leaving only the heterocercal tail as a reminder of their ancient lineage. Abundant in the Triassic, this group rapidly declined towards the end of the Mesozoic era.

The second superorder – the *Holostei* – were for a while the dominant fishes in the middle Mesozoic. Jaws and tails shortened, and their scaled coverings developed variety, most losing their shiny appearance. At this point, the bony fishes first invaded the seas, and the mainstream of evolution for the higher bony fishes flowed into the oceans, where seemingly limitless opportunities existed. This was their contribution. Having accomplished the evolutionary adaptations demanded in the new medium, they enjoyed a brief prosperity. However, it was not for the holosteans to endure until modern times. This group became rare and then almost extinct in the

Cretaceous, leaving species from only two freshwater families to survive. These are the gars and bowfin of North America. Both are represented in southern Canada. The longnose gar is found in the Great Lakes from Lake Huron and down the St Lawrence to below Quebec City. It also occurs in lakes Simcoe and Nipissing as well as the Ottawa River. The spotted gar, a more southern species, has the northern limit of its range in Lake Erie. The bowfin, the sole surviving representative of its family, is found in the St Lawrence watershed and the Great Lakes (with the exception of Lake Superior). Neither gar nor bowfin is much prized for food or sport. They are, however, scientifically interesting survivors from an age before the evolution of the true bony fishes.

The *Teleostei*, the third superorder of the ray-finned fishes, are the true bony fishes. Bodies can be flat, round, elongated, or misshapen. Scales can be large or small, and their fins elaborate, reduced, or even absent. The gills, however, all have a single pair of openings, with bony coverings (opercula). The body is supported by an internal skeleton, which serves also to support the fins with bony rays. The teleosts dominate the fish world. They are at the height of their

The sturgeon (upper left) *is a primitive ray-finned fish. The bowfin* (left), *with its long, spineless dorsal fin, is a survivor of a once dominant order – the holosteans. The sea robin* (below), *though not typical in appearance, is a teleost, one of the higher bony fishes.*

evolution. They form the overwhelming majority of species and contain all of those we find most desirable and familiar. Only eaters of caviar and shark-fin soup need disagree!

Moreover, it is the measure of how closely a species resembles the teleost pattern that determines whether we accept it as 'proper' for food or sport. Eels are teleosts, yet we distrust them as we do a snake; sculpins and sea-robins are teleosts, yet we fear their big-headed ugliness and elaborate fleshy fins. The diminutive sea horse is a teleost yet we express surprise that it should be related to cod, trout, or herring. A young child will unerringly sketch the basic body plan of the typical bony fish. The tail will be roughly symmetrical. The paired pectoral and pelvic fins will be small, the pelvics (used as brakes as well as water circulators), if present, will be behind the operculum. The eye will be large and placed well forward, above the mouth and behind the nostrils. The scales, if present, will be thin, flexible bony structures. The child may, however, mistakenly append a string of bubbles arising from the mouth. Breathing in these fishes is accomplished solely by means of gills folded in pairs inside the mouth cavity.

10 ADAPTATION TO HABITAT

Fishes, mostly the bony kinds, exist now in all the world's waters, ranging in size from tiny, less-than-an-inch-long guppies to fifty-foot whale sharks (aptly named for, though they are truly sharks, they have developed, in a dramatic example of convergent evolution, a manner of feeding similar to the largest plankton-filtering whales). Although most fishes inhabit the sunlit shallower waters, some survive at pressures as great as 18,000 pounds per square inch in the deepest

Carp, like many other fish that feed by ingesting bottom sediments, have underslung mouths and barbels. Their grinding teeth are located in their throats.

parts of the Pacific Ocean. Their body temperatures are those of their particular surroundings. We call them cold-blooded although the night-time angler in tropical seas finds his catch warm to the touch when air temperatures are less than the water. Each fish has its particular temperature tolerance (usually a range of about 13 degrees) though some are wider than others. Unable to adjust its own body temperature, a fish must move to where a suitable temperature exists. This is the basis of many a piscine migration. *Dallia* in the Yukon and Alaska can survive prolonged freezing during the winters. Goldfish (carp) have survived temporary freezing in southern Canada. Certain small minnows found in hot springs in the American southwest live all their lives at a constant 93 degrees. A good example of the effect of temperature in limiting the distribution of certain animals is the 65-degree July isotherm which coincides with the northern limit of both the smallmouth and largemouth bass in Canada.

The great majority of teleosts dwell either in the shallow waters of the continental shelves or in fresh water. Below these are a smaller number of species living at depths intermediate between the surface waters and the ocean bottoms. Few species live in the deepest waters.

Sunlight, which powers the food-making process in the plants upon which animals depend, loses its power as it penetrates into the water. For this reason, the topmost layer of the open ocean or, better still, the shallow coastal areas of the continents, support most of the ocean's life. Close to shore, nutrients eroded from the land-masses fertilize the water. The surface waters are most susceptible to climatic influences especially in the temperate zones. Shallow-water teleosts typically show a constriction of their north-south distributions directly related to temperature.

Deep-water fishes tend to have much wider geographical ranges. If conditions are extreme for the deep-sea denizens, they are at least stable. No storms or tidal waves disturb the primeval darkness. At 250 fathoms, the dominant dwellers are large schools of flattened silvery fishes with eyes large enough to make the most of what little light penetrates. Below this, fishes, mostly dark brown or black in colour, are few and far between. Food is scarce and large populations cannot be supported. Their eyes have regressed (except in those species that have developed luminous organs to shed a little light in the abysmal darkness), and the other senses must take their place. Other extreme specializations have been evolved to allow a few species to pioneer in this watery frontier.

Jet-black female angler fishes survive by dangling a luminous 'bait' between their eyes – and above their ever-open cavernous mouths – whilst tiny males (a mere twentieth of their size) cling parasitically to them. Some deep-sea dwellers hunt far and wide in search of prey and have elastic bellies and unhinging jaws to allow them to swallow giant meals – enough perhaps to last them until the next infrequent opportunity to feed arises.

The deepest bottoms of the oceanic trenches are usually of soft mud, and the little blind fishes which live there have fins ending in long filaments to support them above the ooze.

Angler fish possess a 'fishing pole and lure,' modified from the first dorsal fin spine, which is used to attract prey towards its large mouth.

Varied as fishes are in form, physiology, and distribution, their behaviour likewise covers a considerable spectrum. The forerunners of higher vertebrates, they display most of the behaviour patterns we think more typical of mammals and man. Konrad Lorenz, the famous Austrian ethologist (ethology is the study of innate behaviour patterns in animals), has reported on the stickleback's fierce territorial combats and the struggle for dominance among Chinese fighting fish. Many fish communicate vocally and are much more sophisticated and 'vertebrate' in their actions than most of us – who leave them to drown in air in the bottom of a boat – realize.

11 GLACIAL INVASION

Canada's land mass has a long history of emergence from and reinvasion by the sea. Most of the ancestral fish orders have occupied our submerged landscape at one time or another and many have left fossilized evidence of their passing. Devonian deposits in particular are frequently found across Canada on or near the surface. They are prominent at Percé Rock on the Gaspé and in southwestern Ontario. They make up the rocks of Lake Manitoba and Great Slave Lake. They are scattered throughout the Rockies and can be seen in the 'Ancient Wall' near Jasper and on Norquay and Sulpher Mountains in Banff. Our fishes have been faced with many drastic climatic changes from salt to fresh water and from dry land to ocean or freshwater lake. These events, both locally and on a worldwide scale, have acted as a catalyst to the evolutionary process. During the peak of the last glaciation, the slate of Canadian freshwater fishes was almost entirely wiped clean for glaciers covered 97 per cent of the land. Those species that survived to return (and most did) survived outside of our borders. The freshwater glacial lakes of Canada and the United States were formed during the retreat of the ice masses.

As the great weight of the ice-mass was lifted from the northeastern part of the continent, uplifting occurred and changes in the drainage systems opened up numerous chan-

The frozen land

The map shows the maximum extent of the glaciers during the Ice Age. During the tens of thousands of years that the thick ice covered the land, the advancing glaciers deepened pre-existing valleys and reshaped the hills. When the glaciers retreated for the last time, a new geography emerged – with streams, rivers, and lakes filled by the glacial melt water. The continent once again was green and repopulated with animals and plants.

Fishes re-established their domains by following the new water courses that threaded across the land after the last glaciers pulled back from the Great Lakes region beginning about 14,000 years ago.

The fossil of an ancestor of the goldeye (right) found in British Columbia has been dated at 50 million years. Descendants now live in some large post-glacial lakes.

So-named because of their peculiar muscular stomach, these gizzard shad are normally found in shallow water.

nels through which both salt- and freshwater fish could redistribute themselves. There is reliable evidence to indicate that there were three principal centres of post-glacial dispersal of fishes from the refugia wherein they had survived. There was an eastward movement of Pacific forms from the Alaska-Yukon area; a northward movement from the Mississippi valley; and a westward dispersal from the edge of the Atlantic coastal plain. The present Great Lakes fauna is more closely related to that of the Mississippi watershed than the Atlantic, indicating that the former contributed most of the present fish populations to the Great Lakes. In order to trace the dispersal of fishes from the centres of their origins, ichthyologists have studied the changes in land form and drainage during and since the retreat of the ice. Since Canadian fishes can neither walk nor fly, much has in turn been learned about the history of changing land forms by noting the modern distribution of fishes.

The richness and variety of the Great Lakes fish fauna (173 species) stems not only from the great diversity of its abundant waters – grading from warm to cold, from stagnant to swift, from small ponds and brooks to large rivers and the great inland seas themselves – but also from the diverse origins of the fishes themselves. Some are ancient, some are new. Some are relicts of northern species pushed south by the ice-sheets of the Wisconsin glacier, then trapped in the south and eastward draining Great Lakes watershed by the retreating ice. Much the same factors apply on the larger scale across the entire country. Populations that were pushed south and kept apart by the glaciers sometimes developed into new species and varieties. When the scattered remnants of these isolated communities once more reoccupied Canadian waters, they could sometimes no longer interbreed.

New species evolve fastest in isolation. Some came inland from the Atlantic fresh water refugia via the St Lawrence River. Today there is a large proportion of the freshwater fish fauna of eastern North America represented in the Great Lakes including such 'living fossils' as the lamprey, gars, bowfin, and lake sturgeon.

During the postglacial times there has been a marine invasion of the St Lawrence valley and Lake Ontario. Thirteen thousand years ago, the Laurentide glacier melted back from the St Lawrence lowlands and the Atlantic flowed in. It covered 20,000 square miles of Ontario and Quebec for 4,000 years before starting to drain out via the St Lawrence valley. First, sometime prior to 9,000 years ago, an upheaval west of Quebec City blocked the exit to the ocean and the Champlain sea became for a period a salty lake. Later, the uplifting in the north brought the valley above sea level and the saltwater receded. During the saltwater incursion many species that now exist as freshwater forms entered from the Atlantic Ocean. Among them were the smelt, shad, and alewife, still extant representatives of that marine invasion. As the land rose, the St Lawrence became the main drainage channel for the Great Lakes, causing the river to change progressively from salt to fresh water. It is likely that the anadromous fishes survived the change and that salmon entered Lake Ontario during this transitional period. Their descendants were left to survive as a landlocked population. Lakes in Quebec, the Maritimes, and Maine also acquired similar populations in the same manner. Of all the tens of thousands of the beautiful and desirable salmon which formerly made up the Lake Ontario population, none survived the persecution by man into the present century.

We view the evolutionary history of fishes and other forms with the visual acuity of hindsight. We see just how and where the significant events took place and their consequences. Yet, at the time, the preadaptations which enabled each innovation to take place were always atypical and their possessors usually obscure. One wonders what lowly animal of today might contain the seed of future greatness and perhaps be destined to surpass us. It is a theme beloved of science-fiction writers and is a healthy exercise, indeed, if it in any way increases our appreciation and respect for the lower animals.

D. H. BALDWIN

Camouflage for self-defence

Fish that are preyed upon often rely on camouflage to protect themselves from predators. Mimicing the bottom is also used by predators to conceal themselves while waiting in ambush for their next meal to swim by. The thorny skate (left) usually feeds on bottom-dwelling invertebrates. Its flat body and dull colour often make it invisible from above. The decorated blenny, one of the most spectacular of its family, sports elaborate appendages on its head which mimic the seaweed around it. Similarly, the sculpins (right) are almost invisible against the rocky bottom. Their almost scaleless bodies are shaded to match their environment. Ranging up to two and a half inches, tiny Johnny darters (below) rely on speed as well as inconspicuous markings to protect them from their many enemies.

PART THREE
LIFE IN THE WATER

Life style is a product of both environment and evolution. Most fish are specialists, unable to modify their life styles more than a very little bit. There are precious few Eliza Doolittles in the world of fish.

Canada is one of the largest countries in the world, second in area only to the USSR. Confined within the reach of its boundaries are more than half a million lakes, including Lake Superior, the world's largest. Yet the entire freshwater fish fauna of Canada numbers fewer than 200 species (181 at latest count). By contrast it has been estimated that the freshwater fish fauna of the Amazon River alone is in excess of 2,000 species. Canada's coastline is immense, the second longest in the world. Two recent books summarizing the marine fish of the Canadian Atlantic and Pacific coasts list a total of about 625 species. Adding freshwater and marine species together, Canada's overall total is at least 806 species.

The eggs of the brook trout incubate for fifty to a hundred days, depending upon the water temperature. The larvae remain in the spawning gravel until the yolk is absorbed.

Although the total number of species in the entire world is not known for certain, a good estimate is 20,000 species. Thus Canada's representation in species is a mere 4 per cent of the world's diversity.

Evolution is a process of random chance, working (as a gambler might say) on the percentages. In Canada, the essence of survivorship is at least partly vested in the inherent plasticity and generality of the species. Very few Canadian species can afford the luxury of being extreme specialists. By contrast, there are highly specialized coral reef species: some of the butterfly fish with elongate snouts refuse to eat anything but the tips off polychaete worms, or perhaps only the living polyps of corals.

Why is Canada's environment and the evolutionary history of her fish fauna so restrictive? Canada is cold. That fact alone accounts for many fish that are here, and many that are not. In evolutionary time, Canada has just now been released from an icy prison, the glaciers. Only an instant ago most of her myriad lakes were solid blocks of ice, and no fish lived in them. Truly, the wonder is not how few species there are in Canada, but how many were able to survive the ravages of a series of increasingly intense ice ages.

Fish migrated back into Canada by following the retreating edge of the melting glaciers. Some, trapped here, were lucky enough to have chosen to hide in one of a few special areas (known as glacial refugia) that were not frozen, squashed, or scraped free of all life forms. A few of the species that are present today were brought here by well-meaning, but ill-informed Europeans who wished to import the food or sport fish to which they were accustomed. Others have been moved from their original locality in Canada to new areas, sometimes intentionally, but other times unintentionally. With few exceptions these moves have been failures or disasters. The reasons for the uniformly bad results are contained in what can appropriately be called the life style of the fish. The fish were not a proper part of the environment into which they had been placed, and either did not survive, or displaced native species.

12 THE ABILITY TO LEARN

Are fish intelligent, and if so can they make use of the faculty in altering their life styles? Certainly fish are intelligent. Some species can be trained to discriminate between colours and shapes, to respond to sounds and to obey signals. In others, learning ability seems remarkably lacking. Species that normally school in large numbers have quite fixed behaviour patterns. If they did not, the schools would disintegrate. There are fishes that never learn not to bash their faces against the aquarium walls every time someone passes a hand over the top. Others, such as the largemouth bass, can become real pets, learning to recognize individuals. A stranger approaching the aquarium evokes little or no response. A familiar person is rewarded by an immediate reaction; the bass moves to the place where feeding takes place.

On several occasions while studying smallmouth bass underwater, I have watched a single individual on a nest for days at a time. After about the third day, the guarding male was no longer upset at my approach and during the next few days could easily be trained to accept gentle handling. Any attempt to hurry the process, or any error in handling which frightened the bass, resulted in a great delay in the acceptance of the diver. Fish that have the greatest intelligence seem to be those that in their daily lives require a measure of individuality in adapting to and learning about the environment in which they find themselves.

13 ODDS OF SURVIVAL

In the life of any fish, one of the most vulnerable times is in the early larval stages. Modes of reproduction in fish vary from the simple style of the codfish to complex nest-building of sticklebacks, and to live-bearing fishes such as surfperches. Huge congregations of codfish settle near the bottom and over a period of days or weeks broadcast their eggs and sperm freely into the water. This haphazardness requires staggering numbers of eggs. Consider the odds of survival for any single egg. Assuming that the population of fish is stable in numbers, then over the life of any given pair of fish, only two eggs will survive to adulthood to reproduce. An average codfish lays two million eggs each time it spawns. If the fish spawns an average of five times in its life, then some ten million eggs will have been laid to produce two adults. The codfish egg has only one chance in five million of surviving. Why is the mortality so great? As soon as the codfish (or the herring or any other species that spreads its eggs liberally over the bottom) signals that it is ready to spawn, virtually every other animal in the area moves in to gobble up the free food.

Some eggs float, as in the case of the codfish; others, such as herring eggs, sink and rest on the bottom. Those that rise form a major food item for many other young fish that are already at the surface and searching for food. As soon as the

Mountain streams like this one, formed by the retreating glaciers, offer a special environment. Fish in such areas are adapted to the fast-moving, highly oxygenated, cold water.

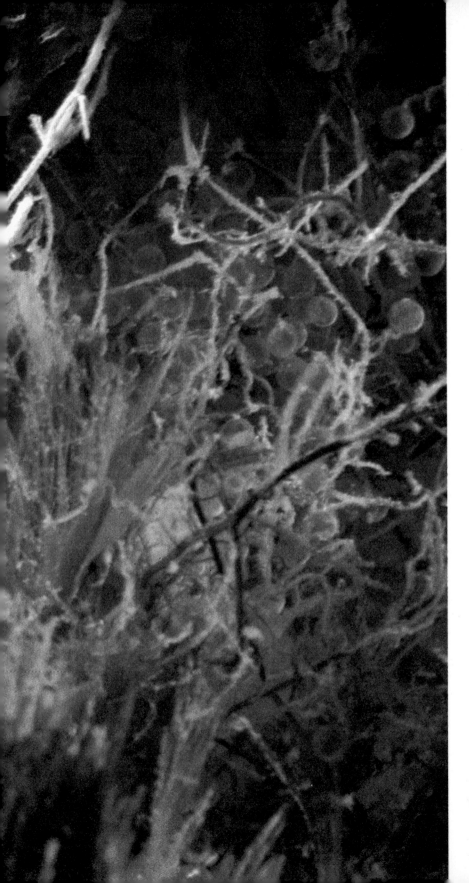

Fish eggs are sometimes joined in a jelly-like mass like the one pictured above, which was washed ashore during a storm, or are scattered singly, but in great quantities (left).

embryos in the egg mature enough to hatch, they begin to wiggle. Soon they break free of the gelatinous membranes that protected them, and by their movement attract the attention of nearby predators which again move in to feed.

Other methods of protecting the eggs, aside from producing huge numbers, include elaborate nest-building and nest-guarding. These techniques are obviously extremely old, because even the most primitive of fishes, the lampreys, build nests by lifting stones from a river bed one at a time and drifting back with them. They then move forward a few inches and repeat the process after having laid their eggs in the pit, burying them as they proceed. They do not care for their young; this requires a more highly developed intelligence, one in which a considerable range of behaviour pattern has developed. Many of the sculpins build nests, or hide their eggs under stones, and then remain on guard until they are hatched. Several of the gunnels (elongate shallow-water ocean species that often hide in the tide-flat weed beds) lay their eggs

61

Mating ritual

The male smallmouth bass builds a nest in gravel in a protected spot on the river or lake bottom by fanning away the finer material. Then, by means of display, rubbing, and nipping, he courts the female (above left). The male bass lowers himself to the nest bottom, anticipating the female which remains above him (centre). When she is ready, she quickly moves parallel to the male, rotates on to her side and, quivering, deposits the eggs. The male carefully pushes the eggs to the nest with his pectoral fin, and then fertilizes them. This is repeated frequently over a two- to four-hour period. The female abruptly races from the nest; the male (left) remains to guard it. When the young hatch, in four to ten days, the male (above) remains with them for several days.

in a tight mass, then gather them close and curl their bodies around the eggs creating a living nest.

A more elaborate nest is built by the members of the sunfish family which includes the black basses. These fish build their nests in very shallow water, and it is often easy to watch the whole procedure including courtship from the shoreline with a pair of field glasses trained on the nest. Black basses spawn in the spring. The event is heralded by about a week of digging and chasing on the part of the male, who prepares a nest varying in size from a few inches across (in the case of the green sunfish) to several large pits up to six feet in diameter (in the case of a black bass). The tiny darters build a mound of pebbles about one to two inches across in which they lay their eggs. Certainly the most impressive nest built in fresh waters in Canada is that of the threespine stickleback. With the onset of spring, the male begins to brighten to a deep

red on his undersurface. He then gathers tiny twigs, little bits of leaves and other vegetation which he moulds into a barrel-shaped little bower. It is hollow, with a smooth circular opening at each end. During this period the male cannot tolerate the approach of another male and will fly immediately to the attack should one approach. Once the nest is ready, the male searches for and courts a female with a series of brilliant displays of colour and stance. Once the female 'agrees' to the proposal, the male impatiently nudges and nips her until she enters the nest to deposit her eggs. Should any of the eggs become dislodged and fall from the nest, the male picks them up and carefully sets them back in place.

Perhaps the most advanced technique of caring for the young until they are old enough to fend for themselves is to retain the eggs in the female's body, bearing them finally as young fish. The Pacific coast surfperches follow this pattern;

The three-spined stickleback, normally greenish-brown, becomes brilliantly coloured during breeding season. The elaborate nest of twigs and plant debris is held together by a kidney secretion of the male, who guards the eggs and young for several days.

however, they provide little or no parental care following the birth of the young fish. Most of the livebearers produce between five and thirty young. This type of birth also requires that the female be fertilized by means of an intromittent organ which the male inserts into her body. In surfperches, copulation occurs about five months before fertilization. The female stores the sperm in a special compartment until the eggs are ripe, then releases the sperm to the eggs. Lest anyone think that copulation is a high order of evolutionary achievement, both the primitive sharks and rays are fertilized internally, and some of the sharks have an extremely efficient placenta-like device for nurturing the young. Some of the young sharks are far less pleasantly disposed; they eat the mother's newly produced eggs as they travel down the oviducts. It has been suggested that if one of the young sharks is considerably larger than its siblings, it could become cannibalistic in its mother's womb, by eating its brothers and sisters.

The eggs of sharks are fertilized internally, and some, like the dusky shark (left), *bear live young. The unborn young of the surfperch* (below) *are sustained on the ovarian fluid, rather than yolk.*

Early life of coho salmon

1 *Searun coho salmon lay from 1,500 to 6,000 large orange-red eggs. After spawning, the eggs are covered by digging and moving gravel from the edge of the nest, and are left to develop deep in the gravel on the bottom of the stream. Soon after spawning, the adults die. Eyes begin to show in the eggs about a month after being deposited.*

2 Depending on the water temperature, the coho eggs hatch within five to eight weeks. The newborn salmon or alevins have large, bulbous abdomens, containing the egg sac or yolk, shaping them to resemble some grotesque insect larva. This yolk is their only means of nourishment for the first few weeks of life.

3 *While hidden for two to three weeks in the relatively safe spawning gravel, where there are few predators, the alevins grow, gradually absorbing the yolk.*

4 *Approaching the final stage of larval life, the alevins have almost completely absorbed the yolk, and will soon venture out to sustain themselves.*

5 *Most fry remain at least a year in the fresh water where they were spawned, competing with other bottom feeders for food.*

6 *In the first year, coho smolts grow to about four inches. Most migrate in small schools to salt water. Those that remain in the fresh water never spawn.*

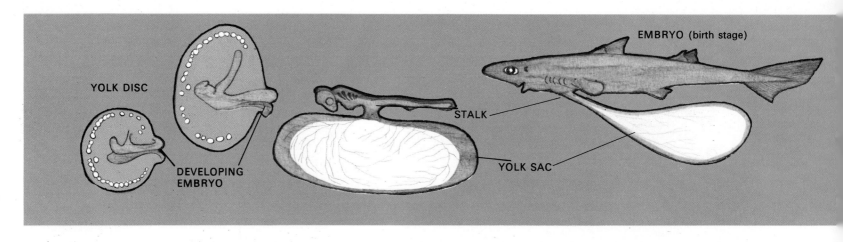

YOLK DISC

DEVELOPING EMBRYO

STALK

YOLK SAC

EMBRYO (birth stage)

Sharks have curious combinations of primitive and advanced characteristics and reproductive systems. Males have claspers on the pelvic fin for internal fertilization. Some sharks, like

Shark reproduction

The dogfish shark embryo (below) is attached to a yolk sac with a long tube or stalk. This sac will provide nourishment for the young shark before and after birth. Eventually the yolk sac will be completely absorbed by the fish. This method of reproduction is similar to that of many snakes and lizards, but differs from mammalian reproduction in that the embryo is not nourished directly by the mother's body.

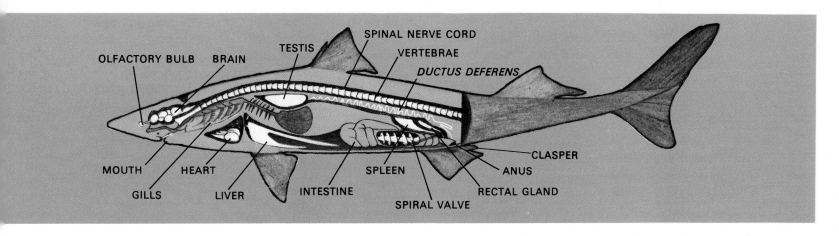

OLFACTORY BULB   BRAIN   TESTIS   SPINAL NERVE CORD

VERTEBRAE

DUCTUS DEFERENS

SPINAL NERVE CORD

CLASPER

MOUTH   HEART   SPLEEN   ANUS

GILLS   LIVER   INTESTINE   RECTAL GLAND

SPIRAL VALVE

the spiny dogfish (below) produce living young, with the embryo developing from the yolk disc, until it lifts away from the yolk, still attached by a stalk. After birth, the young shark is fed from the yolk disc, slowly absorbing it. Fertilization takes place internally in sharks, but not all produce live young. In some, the young develop in an egg case.

14 LIFE IN FRESHWATER LAKES

The richest lakes are those that have the largest extent of shallow water, an optimum level of nutrients, and the longest growing season. These lakes are to be found distant from the Canadian Shield, that vast boulder scraped clean by the glaciers, and in the most southerly parts of Canada such as southern Ontario. The poorest lakes are found over the rocky shield, and in the cold northern parts of the Canadian Arctic. The richness of a lake is often defined in terms of the number of fish that might be harvested annually from it without changing its ecological make-up. A poor lake might yield annually an average of 0.1 pound of fish per acre of lake area without suffering ecological damage. A rich lake in Canada could yield twenty or even fifty pounds per acre. By contrast a culture pond in Asia, one of the richest of aquatic systems, may yield tons per acre annually. The deepest lakes tend to be the poorest. Thus, although Lake Superior contributes as much to the Canadian freshwater fish market as any other lake, its per-acre rate of production is just about the lowest. Despite the fact that it is the largest of the Great Lakes, it does not have the greatest diversity of species – Lake Erie does.

Most of the deep lakes have few species that are able to cope with the eternal cold (39°F at all times of the year) combined with a perpetual murky gloom, or inky blackness, found in their depths. What kind of fish would live in the cold murky depths of a deep inland lake? Muddler, sculpin, lingcod or burbot, bloater: odd names given to odd fish that rest on the exceedingly delicate benthic sediments that will not support the weight of an anchor and which give rise to the many fantastic stories of bottomless lakes. These are the fish that, in a world almost without light, are able to find and feed on the minute benthic insects called chironomids or bloodworms living in burrows in the mud. Deep-living species sometimes have specialized barbels bewhiskering their faces, allowing them to sense, in a way we as humans can never hope to truly understand, the presence of other creatures, including potential mates. Others like the sculpin are spiny, so even if caught by larger fish they make a less than appetizing meal. The deep-water chubs also inhabited these dark regions of the lakes. They have now been virtually wiped out by a combination of pollution, overfishing, and competition from introduced exotic species such as the lamprey and alewife. Theirs was a different mode of life from that maintained by the bottom-resting sculpins and burbots. They swam just above the bottom in what at one time must have been nearly endless numbers. How they sensed their position and prey in that world of quiet, cold, and gloom is a mystery that man will no longer have the opportunity to investigate.

One of the least known yet one of the most important deep-water benthic species is a fish called the trout-perch. The name is quite descriptive; the fish looks just like the improbable combination of a trout and a perch, but is diminutive in size and an almost transparent sandy-brown colour. With its very large eyes, it is adept at moving in the deep, dark waters and occasionally in shallow, muddy rivers. Trout-perch are important because they are a major source of food for many of the larger species such as the lake trout. Lake trout are common in moderately deep water and meet the range of trout-perch as the little forage fish come from the depths into shallower water with nightfall.

Not all the deep-water fish in lakes truly belong there; the rainbow smelt is a newcomer to the Great Lakes (at least beyond Lake Ontario). Originally an oceanic fish, it is certainly responsible in part for many of the bad things that have happened in the lakes, but nonetheless now forms the basis of an important fishery in both Lake Erie and Lake Huron. Smelt are plankton feeders; their mouths truly bristle with teeth, their eyes are large and very sensitive. In fact, their eyes are so sensitive that they are among the very few fish that can maintain a school at night. Schooling of course, is a form of

Smelts (above right) *travel in schools, even at night. During their spring spawning runs, they are a target of dipnet fishermen. The tiny, nearly transparent troutperch* (right) *feeds mainly on insect larvae and is an important forage fish. A relative of the cod, the burbot* (far right) *has several barbels to aid in locating food in the murky depths. It enters shallow water to feed and spawn.*

Near the surface

Fishes living in the regions close to the surface of freshwater lakes have best access to food and light. The walleye (above left) avoids bright sunlight and lives in turbid waters or retreats to the depths during the day. The fathead minnow (centre left) relies on its prolific reproduction to ensure survival against its host of predators. As its name implies, the rock bass (left) favours the rocky regions of shallow lake waters. Like the pumpkinseed (above), it forms schools for protection.

camouflage. Predators must be able to aim at a single individual to be able to catch it. Fish in schools, antelope in herds, and birds in a wheeling flock, all make the individual invisible in their numbers even though the prey is perfectly obvious.

Of the 181 species found in freshwater Canada, most live in the lakes, but of those, fewer than a tenth live in the darkness of limnological depths. The life of an ecosystem is in the sunlight that reaches its plants. A lake is no different. The lighted lake waters below the level of significant wave and ice damage are richest, containing the largest proportion of plants and animals, the greatest diversity of species and the most rapid rate of growth and reproduction. A fisheries scientist who put his net into deep water would be surprised to catch more than four or five species of fish. All would be fish forced to feed on 'leftovers,' the dregs of the rich upper world that drifted down to them. The same net set in shallow water might yield twenty to twenty-five different species. The diets of these fish would include plants, the many kinds of small bottom insects and crustaceans, crayfish, frogs, leeches, and even other fishes. What are the shallow-water fish? They are the bait stealers, the tiddlers, the minnows, the perch, bass, trout, walleye, and pike. They are also the less commonly known ones, like the mudminnow, the quillback carpsucker, the sand darter, the tadpole madtom, the cutlips minnow, and the greater redhorse. All of them, rare or common, large or small, share not only the energy that streams into their world in the form of sunlight, but also the space in which they coexist.

Mid-day is the least active part of any of the daylight hours, but most fish will feed at any time prey are easily available. Thus, a fisherman who has just the perfect bait and presents it to a pike in just the right way can usually induce the pike to take it no matter what the time of day. But there are certain times of day when the fish are keyed to take food. For most large predators, this is at dusk or dawn. At noon, however, predators are usually resting gently on the bottom. Sometimes they hover over the bottom, or join schools of lesser species. At mid-day, the small fish are very active. The lake darters, shallow water sculpins, and the young of the sunfishes move slowly, seemingly preoccupied, picking at the bottom, and at the twigs and other places where their tiny food organisms are hiding. Oftentimes this is done under the very

nose of a potentially deadly pike or bass. Surprisingly, there is danger involved; but because the minnows, darters, and other small fish are all tuned to it, and ready to respond rapidly, that danger is not imminent.

By the end of the daylight hours the situation changes quickly. The small fish have fed and are ready to find a resting place for the night. The tendency to maintain schools is starting to break down as the light continues to fail. Because the schools function at least partly to camouflage the individual, the predators now start to move. This further complicates the situation for the prey fish, because now the danger is imminent, now the pike is in unpredictable motion. The light is failing and the slow powerful strokes of the giant's tail are of too low a frequency for the little fish to hear its approach. Moreover, the pike is in perfect tune: his eyes are particularly sensitive to movement, and his nerves are ready to react with incredible swiftness to the motion of a sunfish or minnow panicked into flight by the looming approach of sudden death.

In Canadian lakes, where underwater twilight is perhaps two hours in length, the frantic switch from daytime activities to night is completed in about one and one-half hours. Compared to a coral reef, this is extremely prolonged. There the period can be measured in minutes. After darkness, the night shift takes over with their special set of duties. The pike, his hunger satisfied, now slows his movements and begins to search for a resting place. His efforts are not desperate. Not only does he have little to fear, but also he is still alert to the chance that he may pick up an early stray of the night shift which has arrived before the cover of darkness is complete.

It is very difficult to give a complete description of what goes on under the cover of darkness in the shallow waters of a lake. It is only within the last very short while that scientists have been able to observe at first hand what occurs, and the data is far from complete. A diver entering the water quietly enough not to disturb what is going on would find a strangely quiet place. At first, looking in the familiar areas, waiting for the approach of a curious sunfish or bass, he would wonder where all the fish had gone. Glancing to the bottom, however, he would find it often literally carpeted with fish. All of these fish are resting in a state of considerably slowed metabolism.

Nesting fish

Many shallow-water fish build nests to protect their eggs. Two that build quite different nests are the three-spined stickleback (above), which is found in coastal rivers and lakes, except some *northern ones, and the bluegill (right),* a large and colourful sunfish, found only in eastern and central North America in shallow warm water of ponds and small rivers.

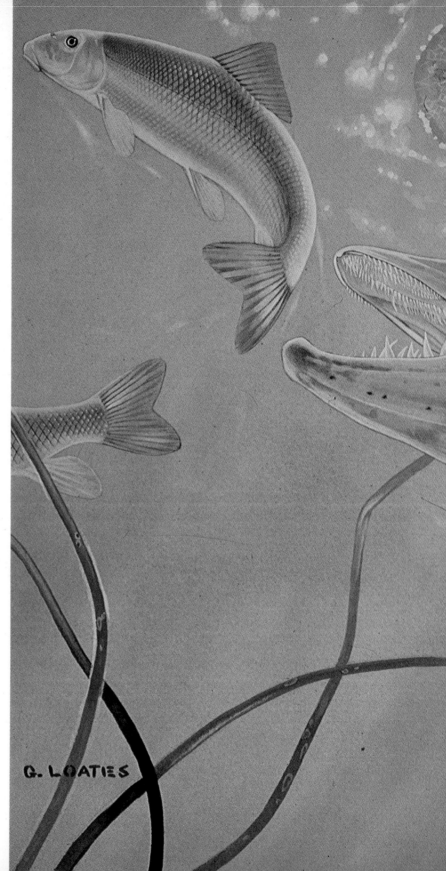

Freshwater predators

The pike (above) *and the muskellunge* (right), *a member of the pike family, share many attributes. They are both highly prized game fish and offer a challenge to fishermen, as evidenced by the ones that escape, such as this pike with the lure in its mouth. Both pike and muskie are found in warm, heavily vegetated waters. During the height of the summer heat, pike normally move into deep water, whereas the muskie seem to appreciate the warmer water found in the shallows.*

Adults, with their size and secretive habits, have only man and lampreys as enemies. They are fierce predators, who will eat almost anything that comes their way. They strike prey fishes from the side so that they can take them into their mouths sideways, and then retreat to a sheltered spot where they rotate the captured fish and swallow it head first.

These fish compete with each other for food, space, and spawning sites in areas they both inhabit. The pike has a much larger range, however, covering much of inland Canada.

G. LOATES

I have found it quite easy at such a time to reach down quietly and pick up a fish in my hands. This same fish in the daytime would not allow approach closer than a distance of some feet. They have no eyelids, so appear no different than in the daytime, but they act very little different from a person rudely disturbed in his sleep. Placed gently back down on the bottom, they bumble about slowly, knocking their noses on rocks or twigs, and giving one the precise impression of having 'stubbed their toes.' If they are frightened, they move off at a frantic pace, but are so confused that they are just as likely to run into the very diver who so frightened them in the first place.

As well as the sleeping fish, there are the janitors and night-time burglars of the fish world. Suckers, with their vacuum cleaner mouths, drift in from the deeper waters after the fullness of night to sweep gently over the bottom muds, look-ing for the small crustaceans that are their food. The care-taking duties are shared by a number of the fish that come from deeper water at night. But not all of the fish that move into the shallows at night are as friendly. In fact, some are moving in with the specific goal of feeding on both the janitor-ial night staff and the sleeping daytime fish. One of these burglars is the burbot, a denizen of the deeps that cannot adequately support itself on a diet derived solely from the lower depths, and moves into the shallower waters to supple-ment its intake.

Those living in the depths essentially live in a world of left-overs, leftover plankton, leftover nutrients, all drifting down slowly from the rich lighted waters. In between is the pelagic realm, not well exploited in Canadian lakes. The whitefish and those ancient forms that look so much like the whitefish, the goldeye and mooneye, share the vast stretches between

During the daylight hours many varieties of small fish are at the peak of their activity, often travelling in schools as they leisurely swim about locating food. They are constantly aware of the dangers around them, and are alert to any movement.

the top and bottom of the lake with some of the newcomers, particularly the alewife in the Great Lakes, an invader from the ocean. In the Great Lakes of Africa, by comparison, there are fish of many families and species, that have taken a wide variety of shapes and sizes, specializing in the pelagic plankton-rich habitats. Some of the African cichlids are mackerel-like, some look like the oceanic damselfishes. Their diversity is amazing, and is a product of the long time in which evolution has had to operate in the Great Lakes of Africa. Canada's Great Lakes have had virtually no time, and very few parallels have developed since the glaciers. Indeed, Canada's evolutionary history is so recent and active, particularly in her whitefishes, that recent books have difficulty defining some of the species. This fact is testimony to the dynamic nature of evolution highlighted by our attempts to impose a static system of classification.

15 FLOWING RIVERS

Are rivers so different? In a sense they are quite different; they are open-ended ecosystems, something a little unusual in nature which normally bases its livelihood on saving the last scrap of everything. Few fish that can live in a river cannot live at least for a short time in a lake. Two which have difficulty are little minnows. One is *Rhinichthys cataractae*, the longnose dace, and the other, even more extreme in shape, is *Platygobio gracilis*, the flathead chub. These intriguing little fellows boast a very racy shape, and an almost shovel-shaped head. The neanderthal slope to their foreheads acts as a partial hydrofoil to keep the fish close to the bottom where

With approaching darkness, schools of fish disperse in search of refuge. Shallow-water predators, like the pike, take advantage of this confusion. With nightfall, they, too, will seek resting places.

SMALLMOUTH BASS

MINNOWS

PICKEREL

PIKE

PUMPKINSEED

ROCK BASS

A trout stream

These divers are preparing to enter the chilly waters of Wilmot Creek, Ontario, to photograph its underwater life. They are certain to discover quite a variety of fish, including three different types of trout. The pair of rainbow trout (below) have stationed themselves in a sheltered spot under a log, waiting for food to come drifting down with the current. They are darker in colour than those found in lakes and generally do not attain the size and weight of lake-dwellers. The brook, or speckled trout (upper right) *require clear, cool water, and are known to move downstream to larger bodies of water when temperatures rise. Brown trout* (lower right) *were introduced into Canadian waters from Europe in the 1880s, mainly into stream or river habitats, but a number of lake or sea-run populations also exist now.*

The logperch (above) *differs from others of its family in that it inhabits the waters of large lakes. The male rainbow darter* (right), *one of Canada's most colourful small fishes, is well adapted to life on the river bottoms.*

has legendary ability to withstand cold. In 1886, a scientist wrote, 'the vitality of these fishes is astonishing. [Frozen specimens] which are thrown to the ravenous [Eskimo] dogs are eagerly swallowed; the animal heat of the dog's stomach thaws out the fish whereupon its movements soon cause the dog to vomit it up alive.' Modern scientists have found that although it can withstand unusual cold, this fish cannot survive freezing solid.

There are lake fish which could not survive in a river. Many of the pelagic or free-ranging lacustrine forms would find the constant rush of water an impossible situation to cope with for very long. In small rivers where drifting organisms are rare, they would find little food. There is one species of sculpin regularly found in stream areas, but even this refugee from deep water cannot handle the buffeting of a riffle, as the specialized minnows and darters can.

In these two habitats live all 181 species of Canadian freshwater fish. Perhaps 10 per cent live in the depths of the lakes, a further 15 per cent are primarily river-dwellers, and the rest live in the quiet, shallow waters of our lakes.

16 OUR THREE OCEANS

the current is least rapid. The longnose dace is sometimes found in the near-shore surf area of lakes, a habitat similar to a fast-running river. A whole family of fish, the darters (Etheostomidae), evolved specifically to live in rivers, with one exception in Canada, the logperch, a common lake darter. They now number about fifteen species in Canada and about twice that in the United States. They are found nowhere else in the world, but are endemic to North America, together with the sunfishes (family Centrarchidae). The darters, unlike most fishes, have no air bladder so they sit weighted to the bottom, another adaptation to river life. Most of these fish have higher than usual oxygen needs, which they can satisfy only in the rapidly moving and highly oxygenated river water.

There is another intriguing little fish common in the weedy sluggish areas of rivers in the far north. The blackfish *Dallia*

How much of the ocean belongs to Canada is a question that has at least three sides to it: legal, geological, and biological. At present, the legal limits of various countries range from three miles to 200 miles depending upon the vagaries of political thought. Most geologists would say that the limit of the Canadian ocean was at the edge of the continental shelf. This distance is at a minimum on the Pacific coast, and a maximum off Newfoundland. Biologists, on the other hand, would likely not give you a definite answer but would instead suggest that those species that regularly inhabit water shallower than about 600 feet could logically be considered part of the Canadian fauna.

Canada has three oceans bordering her shores: the Arctic, the Atlantic, and the Pacific. Each ocean has its own complement of species, decided by the environment and the geologi-

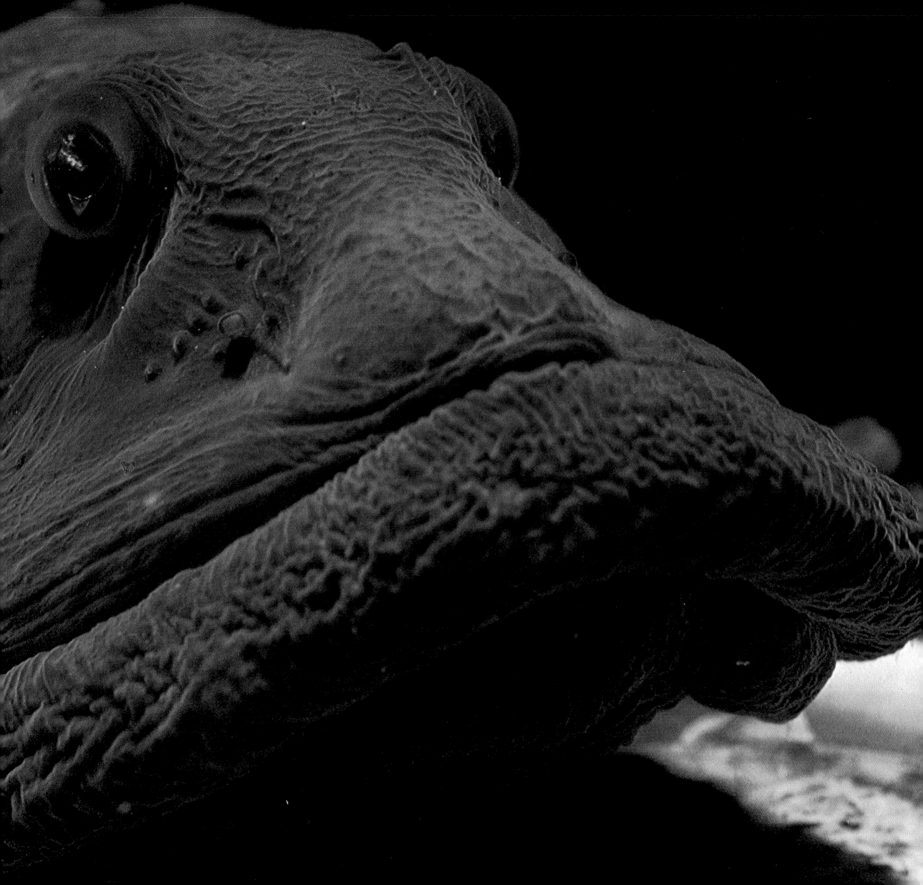

cal history of the area. The Arctic has the fewest species because it has the harshest environment and the most severe and restrictive geological history. Its fishy inhabitants, aside from the anadromous salmons and whitefish, belong mainly to two particularly hardy groups of fish, the sculpins (family Cottidae) and the eelpouts (family Zoarcidae), with scattered representatives from other families of fish. All Arctic species lead a sedentary, quiet existence. Some burrow in the sediments, such as the eelpouts, but most of the others move with an icy slowness, carefully picking their way across the ocean bottom. Pursued by a diver, they have enough energy to make a single dash for freedom, or at the most two. They then wait, exhausted, to be scooped up easily into a net.

Arctic waters house some of the strangest-appearing fish in the world. The lumpfish looks much like a football with ridges, the diminutive snailfish has an effective suction cup on its belly which is used to hold it tightly to a frond of kelp or a small stone. Most Arctic species are small. *Aspidophoroides monopterygius*, or alligator fish, a member of the sea poacher family, is often smaller in total length than its impressive name when set in type. A few, such as the greenland shark, reach a large size. Very few are able to be active all the time, but at least one species, the polar cod, has found an answer to the question of how to exploit the little creatures that live in the surface waters. Instead of having to swim to reach them, this little fish rides the icebergs. An iceberg does not look like a refrigerator ice cube; the undersides are very pitted and full of cracks. The polar cod hides in ambush in the cracks, his silvery grey body camouflaging perfectly against the icy greyness of an overhead berg.

There is still colour in the Arctic water despite the crushing cold which slows all life. Several of the eelpouts are almost garish, especially during reproduction. In one species, the throat turns a deep blue-purple colour, while the head becomes suffused with orange, both of which fade towards the tail into a pale buff colour.

The Arctic Ocean joins the Atlantic and the Pacific and draws the species that inhabit it from both of these oceans. There is no good estimate of the number of species of fish in the Arctic Ocean, but it would be less than one hundred. The only species naturally common to both coasts are those which

As befits a coldwater sea-bottom dweller, the common eelpout (left) *has a very large mouth with which to capture its often infrequent meals. The lumpfish* (above), *also a bottom-dweller found in northern waters, often clings to lobster pots and feeds on small invertebrates.*

inhabit the Arctic. Thus, the Northwest Passage, a major stumbling block to shipping, is also a major barrier to the migration of fish from one ocean to another. Why do both of these oceans support a greater diversity of fish life styles than the common ocean? The Atlantic richness in diversity is derived from its extensive shallow-water habitats. In the Pacific there is not the same extent of shallow water, but this lack is balanced by the considerably longer time which the Pacific coast has had for undisturbed evolution. If one accepts the idea of continental drift, the Pacific ocean is old whereas the Atlantic is a new ocean.

The North Atlantic coast sports some species that do not properly belong there. A warm current from the tropical

Atlantic occasionally makes its way up the coast and past the Gulf of Maine, carrying with it an assortment of species whose life style fits them for a coral reef. These fish are expatriates; that is, they are lost forever from their proper habitat, but by a fluke are able to survive in the summer waters off the Canadian coasts. They will never reproduce in the cold waters of our north Atlantic. Some rather startling forms have reached our east coast, including the green moray, largest of the western Atlantic morays, halfbeaks and flying fishes, coronet fish (a strange elongate fish with an enormous snout used in precisely the same manner as a 'slurp gun'), and seahorses. There are others as well, such as the red grouper, the spotfin butterfly fish, and the famous Sargassum fish, a bizarrely coloured angler fish which resembles very closely a piece of weed from the Sargasso Sea. In fact, if one were to remove from the list of Atlantic fishes all those which are strays, the size of that list would be considerably reduced. This would not be true of the list of Pacific fishes, which would be reduced only slightly.

The difference in habitat availability on the two coasts is indicated by the different types of fish found on each. The Pacific is rugged, rocky, and steeply sloping, whereas the Atlantic has smoothly graded slopes, broken only intermittently by rocky areas. One would expect therefore to find more fish adapted to life in a rocky habitat on the Pacific, and more that are characteristic of smooth sand, mud, and gravelly slopes on the Atlantic. This is in fact the case. Of three families of fishes particularly characteristic of rocky areas, the rockfishes (Scorpaenidae), the sculpins (Cottidae), and the poachers (Agonidae), ninety-five species inhabit the Pacific coast, while only nineteen are found on the Atlantic. Five times as many species of this type of fish are found on the Pacific coast as on the Atlantic.

The vast underwater pastures of the Atlantic continental shelves are grazed by (or at least were grazed by) incredible numbers of codfish. In the shallow-to-moderately-deep waters, there are about twenty different species of cod-like fishes. By contrast, there are only five such species on the Pacific coast, or only a quarter as many. Other abundant fishes on the Atlantic coast are rays, flounders, sculpins, and sharks.

How do members of the codfish family (Gadidae) make a living? They include haddock, whiting, pollock, hake, cusk, rockling, tomcod, and burbot, as well as the cod. They are all predacious fishes, feeding heavily on the bottom organisms and on smaller fishes. Many have barbels on their chins which they use to sense the presence of prey organisms hidden in the mud. Most species are elongate and a bit sluggish, tending to move slowly over the bottom in great schools or to hide among the boulders that stick up through the mud. Some get to be of great size; the Atlantic cod is said to have reached 200 pounds in weight. Two of the cods, each quite different, have left the bottom, sluggish habits and become semi-pelagic. These are the whiting and the pollock, which are both voracious predators on small fish. Most predators move singly or in small groups, but in the case of the pollock and whiting, there is enough food available that they can move in very large schools. Because of this habit, they and several other schooling codfish are themselves the object of a voracious predator, man the fisherman. John Cabot's oft-quoted statement that the fish were so abundant off the Grand Banks, one had only to lower a weighted basket into the water to catch them, while probably an exaggeration, is an indication of the size of the schools that at one time swam off the Atlantic coasts of Canada.

Although far less is known about the life history of the rays and the flounders, they are even more tied to the bottom. Their bodies are flattened in the extreme. Rays appear to be flattened from top to bottom, with the head so flat that the gill openings are spread to the side. To circumvent the problem of breathing mud, a set of spiracles on the top of the head sucks clean water down to the gills. It is then pumped out into the bottom muds. The flatfish, on the other hand, have attacked the problem from another angle. They simply lie down on their sides. Presumably the first fish to do that had one of his eyes looking straight into the mud. Young flounders still have the eyes on both sides of the head, but as they

One of the most bizarre of the bottom dwellers, the red Irish lord sculpin (right), *walks slowly across the bottom on fanlike pectoral fins, protected by its spiny head and sharp dorsal spines.*

grow up, the eye migrates around to sit beside the other on one side of the head, at which time they roll over on their sides and settle to the bottom. Each species is quite consistent in which eye goes to which side. Breathing is, of course, no problem, because unlike the rays which have their mouths pointing straight down, the flatfishes have theirs pointing straight forward. Both groups of fish eat much the same thing: snails, clams, worms, crabs, and small fishes. One of the flatfishes, the Atlantic halibut, has reversed the process of flattening to some extent and spends far less time on the bottom than do the other flounders. The extra musculature makes him more rounded in cross-section, and thus more streamlined for speed. As a young fish, the halibut feeds on much the same food as all flounders, but after reaching about two feet in length it feeds almost exclusively on fish. As with

many of the fish in the cool waters of the North Atlantic and North Pacific, the halibut does not reach maturity until ten years old (codfish mature at about five years old, redfish – sold as ocean perch – at about ten years, at which time they are some nine inches in length).

Life on the Pacific coast is more like a game of hide and seek. There are very few wide open stretches that can accommodate huge schools of fish. The most diverse and abundant families of fish on the west coast are the sharks and rays (about half as many as on the Atlantic coast), the surfperches (none on the Atlantic), the blennioid fishes (about twice as many as the Atlantic), the greenlings (none in the Atlantic), and the scorpaenids, sculpins, and poachers (which combined total about five times as many as on the Atlantic side). The additional diversity in the Pacific is in groups of fishes that hide in the rocks or among the weeds. One group, the surfperches, are specialists in living in the rough shoreline surge areas. They are common in the shallows near the docks and pilings on the west coast. Most are at least partly omnivorous (eating both plant and animal material), with mussels,

Left: *A male kelp greenling.*
Below: *The adult flounder lies on its side, with both eyes projecting upwards.*

barnacles and other small crustaceans forming the major part of the diet. Blennioid fish are usually quite elongate with the dorsal and anal fins stretching from near the head to near the tail. Sinuous in movement and secretive in habit, they have life histories which are very poorly known. They include the ronquil, the kelpfish, all the pricklebacks, warbonnets, gunnels, the wolfeel, the wrymouths and the quillfish. Many of the highly coloured species are extremely interesting aquarium specimens as they have complex behaviour patterns when fighting and courting. The purpose of these mock battles is to allow a dominant individual to prove himself, with fierce displays of colour, stance and rushing attacks, but at the same time to prevent the loser from actually sustaining any major injury. Thus, no significant loss of numbers to the population occurs.

Snailfish and lumpsuckers are members of the Liparidae family and have large suction discs formed from the pelvic fins on their ventral surfaces. Most of them have a wide range of depth distribution, and therefore seem to be quite adaptable in their environmental needs, and are often abundant. Most liparids are small, however, and escape casual notice. Very little detail is known of the life history, but it is thought that at least some of them protect the eggs by holding them in their mouths during incubation.

Although there are nearly a hundred species of rockfish, sculpins, and poachers on the Pacific coast, the details of only a few of their life histories are known. Rockfish are often brilliantly coloured in red, orange, and shades of brown, and are usually festooned with an impressive armament of spines. Despite the rather garish appearance of some of their members, they are very good fish to eat. At least several of the rockfish have the ability to make rapid changes in colour. In this way, they can communicate their mood to other members of the species. These colour changes are also used for camouflage over the weedy, rocky areas where they are found.

In addition to the obvious canine teeth in the front of the mouth, the blennioid wolf eel (left) has large grinding teeth in the back of the mouth. Another blennioid fish, the rock gunnel (right), displays the typical elongated fins.

Sculpins, which look much like the rockfish, are another abundant form on the west coast. As might be expected, their food habits and general ecology are also very similar. There is, however, one bizarre sculpin that has a most appealing colour pattern and body shape. It has a ridiculously fat tummy and ungainly trunk with an almost humpbacked appearance, and eyes that look forward over a protruding snout. Oblique bars of alternating light and dark brown terminate with an impudent flash of brilliant red which covers the tail. The name grunt sculpin is derived from the peculiar hissing or grunting noise that it makes when handled. Although it is quite capable of swimming like a normal fish, it spends a good deal of its time crawling over the rocks and fronds of kelp in the shallow tide pools where it is common.

Most of the fish discussed so far are typical of the shallow parts of the ocean. If we consider that 'Canadian' oceans extend to about two hundred fathoms, many of the fish included in the list of Canadian species could be described as deep sea monsters. It would be giving away secrets, of course, to point out that most of these so-called monsters are small;

few exceed a couple of inches in length. The depth limit suggested does not include the truly deep-living creatures, living in regions completely devoid of any trace of sunlight. But it does include creatures able to produce a type of light called bioluminescence, which is common to a great many animals. Although biologists are still not positive of the origin of bioluminescence in the evolutionary tree, they are coming to the conclusion that it must have been very early, probably in single-celled animals. Its purpose is thought to have been to get rid of oxygen (a poisonous substance to those extremely primitive organisms). Modern creatures use it for just about any conceivable purpose: spotlights to find prey, a means of recognizing mates, a lure to bring prey close, a squirted jet of brightly lit liquid to confuse an attacking predator. All of these and many more are evolutionary 'bright' ideas on how to make use of an obsolete technology. There is no plant life at these depths, so these fish exist on the rain of organic debris from the rich, lighted areas of the ocean. Most of them have the ability to turn digestion on and off, making use of the ingested prey only when they actually

need it. Also, because most of the prey is essentially ambushed, these fish are not heavily muscled for long chases. Indeed, some of them probably can swim only very slowly.

Many species make the best of two worlds, by moving up from the almost sterile depths to the crowded cornucopia of the surface waters under the cover of darkness to feed. They retreat with the light of dawn into the icy cold and shadowy world five hundred to a thousand feet below. Consider the energy that is required to swim these distances every night, to adjust to the physiological shock of great temperature changes, and, perhaps most impressive of all, to expel through the complex network of blood vessels surrounding part of the air bladder enough gas to allow for a 1,000-foot change in water depth. Then, in the same night, these fishes turn around and retreat that same distance. The return trip requires that the fish work to resorb that much gas again from the water. Just how much gas is involved? If you had a rubber balloon one foot in diameter at a thousand feet underwater, and released it to go to the surface, by the time it broke through the waves it would be on the order of forty feet in diameter. The increase in size is due to the release of pressure from the overlying water and also to the warming water, both of which allow the air in the balloon to expand.

As in the lakes, less than 10 per cent of the species live in the profundal depths of the ocean. Indeed in the entire world, of which some 55 per cent is covered over with ocean waters of profundal depth, there exist fewer than about 2,000 deep-sea species. It is a difficult place to make a living.

Almost equally difficult a place to live is in the waters directly above these profundal depths–pelagia. These are the crystal-clear offshore waters, waters so clear they are often a purple colour. The purple appears to be opaque, it is so intense. But swim in it, or drop something overboard, and the extreme transparency of the water can be seen. Here, at least within several hundred miles of shore, live the vast numbers of small plankton-feeding herrings, argentines, and other silvery grazers of the sea. Here, too, are the giants of the sea, the incredibly aggressive offshore sharks, the tunas, and the swordfish and marlins, swiftest of all fish. Many of these pelagic species must swim constantly, and would suffocate without the constant rush of water over their gills, because, unlike the inshore species, they have no means of pumping water over them. Some species have muscles so solidly packed that the constant exertion causes a tremendous build-up of heat. Taking advantage of the excess of heat, these animals have evolved a counter-current blood vessel system which concentrates the heat in those constantly contracting muscles, resulting in an essentially warm-blooded fish. This ability is quite remarkably developed in the tunas, the marlins, and in the Isurid sharks (such as the white shark, mako, and porbeagle). They can maintain a body temperature within two or three degrees of 86° F in water temperatures as low as 43° to 50° C. For this reason many of these giants of the sea are worldwide in distribution. Their aggressiveness is based upon the short and usually sparse food chain which exists in the open ocean: when food presents itself, it must be eaten immediately; the next meal may be a very long time off. This is why swimmers, voluntary or otherwise, have so much trouble with the offshore sharks which are large, aggressive, and always hungry.

ALAN R. EMERY

A poor swimmer, the peculiar grunt sculpin (left) *lives on the bottom and often crawls about on rocks by means of its large pectoral fins.*
Right: *A sand tiger shark.*

Game fish

The beautiful grayling (above and right) *is in the same family as trouts, salmons and whitefish. Its former name,* Thymallus signifer, *refers to its distinctive odour, similar to that of wild thyme, and to its flag-like dorsal fin* (signifer: *standard-bearer*). *The grayling is a truly northern fish. It grows rapidly during the short Arctic season, feeding almost entirely on land insects, such as ants, bees and wasps, or on bottom organisms.*

Although the Arctic grayling has been relatively safe in its isolated habitat, its appeal as a spirited game fish will surely bring on anglers and sportsmen.

When one considers that the grayling and most other freshwater fishes of Canada are only recent arrivals in geological time, that they have entered the continent only after the retreat of the last glaciation, the plight of the major sport fishes becomes even more poignant.

The Arctic char (above right) *was once of economic importance only to the coastal Eskimos as a source of food; in recent years it has become the basis of major commercial fisheries and has become a gourmet delicacy. These anadromous fish may exhibit a myriad of colour combinations when they spawn in the fall. The Arctic char that are found in Quebec lakes – sometimes called Quebec red trout* (above) – *are perhaps the most spectacular, and are best known for their spawning displays. The female and male red trout* (left) *show the transformation of colour and shape that take place during spawning. The Quebec Arctic char are considered endangered if not near extinction.*

Efforts to increase the propagation of trout and char have included such activities as stocking lakes and rearing artificially fertilized eggs in hatcheries. Artificial cross-breeding has also been attempted. This is not a new idea – it has been going on in North America for as long as seventy-five years. The cross between a male speckled (or brook) trout and a female lake trout has produced a fertile hybrid (right) *called a splake or wendigo (the Quebec adaptation is* moulac), *which is less susceptible to lamprey attacks.*

PART FOUR
MYSTERIES OF MIGRATION

On July 12, 1946, an American shad – a member of the herring family – was taken in a trap and tagged in its spawning grounds west of Green Island, opposite the mouth of Quebec's Saguenay River. On July 11, 1947, a year less only a day later, the same shad was recaptured in the same trap in exactly the same location.

It is thought that most shad from this spawning ground journey to feeding grounds somewhere between the Gulf of Maine and the Nova Scotia banks. Total round-trip distance: between 1,500 and 2,000 miles. Presumably this particular fish also made the circuit. Odds against its hanging back and not migrating with the rest are too great.

However, it is not known for certain that *this* shad made such a mind-boggling tour. For it to be certain, the fish would have to have been caught and recorded near its feeding grounds. Then, and only then, might it be possible to make

The migration of salmon from salt to fresh water is one of the best known and most studied of the fish migrations. Each spawning season, salmon head upstream to lay their eggs.

correct statements about the migration and homing ability of shad.

This incident is quoted because it illustrates so well our present knowledge of fish migration. There is a body of tantalizing facts that, if only they could be clarified in their relationships, would present us with migrations rivalling any of those in the bird class for long-distance travel and miracles of navigation.

Even historical speculation about fish migration is hard to come by. Addressing himself to the mysterious appearance of eels, Aristotle concluded that they were not the offspring of Jupiter as commonly believed, but that they were sexless, and arose from *gas entera*, the entrails of the sea.

Later, Pliny the Elder imagined that they reproduced themselves by rubbing against rocks, and that the loose pieces of skin grew into eels. Until the eighteenth century, it was believed that they sprang spontaneously from mud. It was impossible even to conceive of migration.

One of the most charming interpretations of fish migration was entertained by the Tlingit and Haida native peoples of western Canada. They imagined that salmon were a race of

99

supernatural beings who lived in human form, feasting and dancing, beneath the sea. Each year these supernatural beings assumed the bodies of salmon, and ascended the streams to sacrifice themselves for the benefit of mankind. *First Salmon* ceremonies were held every year to welcome the new visitors and to commemorate the first sacrifices.

More scientific ideas began to develop in the nineteenth century. Two Italian scientists, working in the Strait of Messina, established beyond a doubt that flat, transparent creatures cast up in masses on shore were larvae of the grown eel. This inferred some form of migratory journey.

In the same period, F. Buckland, in his *Natural History of British Fishes*, put forward an explanation for the apparent homing ability of salmon. His theory has been maintained, more or less, to this day.

'When the salmon is coming in from the sea,' he wrote, 'he smells about till he scents the water of his own river. This guides him in the right direction, and he has only to follow up the scent, in other words, to "follow his nose," to get up into fresh water, i.e., if he is in a travelling humour. Thus a salmon coming up from the sea into the Bristol Channel would get a smell of water meeting him. "I am a Wye salmon," he would say to himself. "This is not the Wye water: it's the wrong tap, it's the Usk. I must go a few miles further on," and he gets up steam again.'

17 SEASONAL AND SPAWNING MIGRATIONS

Most fishes migrate to some degree. For instance, the brilliantly hued redfish of our eastern waters regularly rises from its place on the bottom to feed near the surface at night. Otherwise, it is a steadfast bottom-squatter. Individual redfishes are regularly recaptured at places of release after years of freedom.

Technically, this vertical trip is a migration. (The term comes from the Latin *migrare*, meaning to go from one place to another.) In autumn, when the lake trout leave the cold depths of freshwaters across Canada to spawn in the shoals,

The homeward journey of chinook salmon

The return of mature chinook salmon to their home spawning grounds is one of the most spectacular of the fish migrations. After they reach maturity in the Pacific ocean, they head toward the major rivers of the west coast, often travelling great distances.

Spawning time varies with the time of arrival, the area, and the length of the river migration. In the Fraser River, it takes place from July to November; in the Yukon, in July and August; elsewhere on mainland British Columbia, the time is from August to September; and on Vancouver Island, spawning takes place in October. The distance the fish swim upstream also varies from a short distance just above tidal influence to as much as 600 miles in the Fraser and over 1,200 in the Yukon.

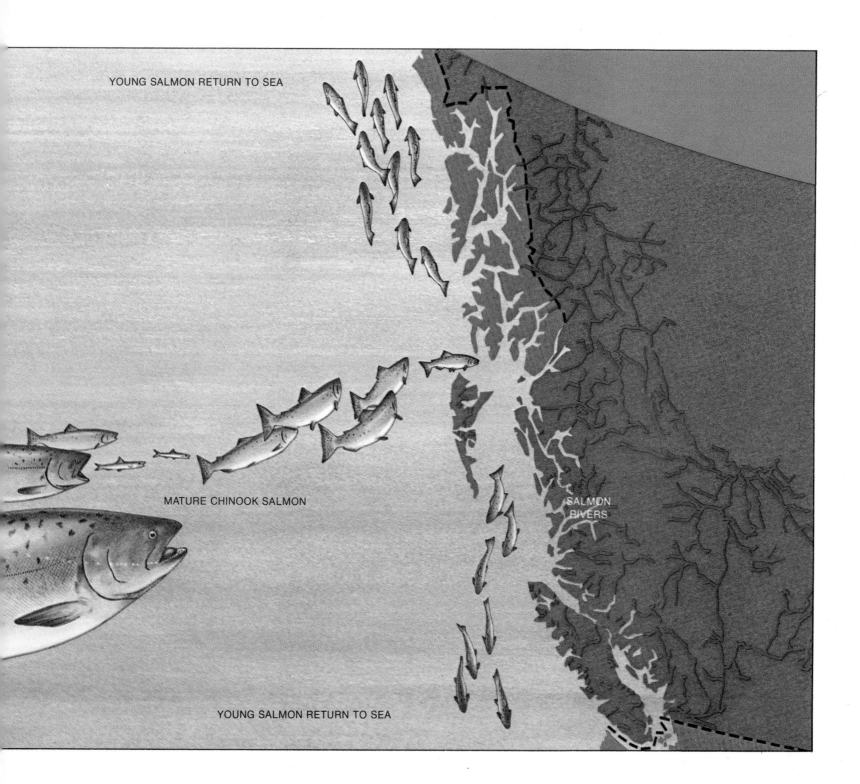

YOUNG SALMON RETURN TO SEA

MATURE CHINOOK SALMON

SALMON RIVERS

YOUNG SALMON RETURN TO SEA

TUNA

HERRING

ATLANTIC WOLFFISH

SCULPIN (Atlantic sea raven)

DOGFISH SHARK

COD

REDFISH

HADDOCK

FLOUNDER

SAND LANCE

MACKEREL

SALMON

CAPELIN

SILVER HAKE

Between ocean and land

The continental shelves skirt most of the earth's coasts, sloping gently away from the shore to a depth of about 500 feet. The shelf is often quite wide, extending more than 100 miles into the sea; some areas, such as off southeastern Florida, have no shelf.

The food supply is so rich on these shelves, where sunlight can usually penetrate right to the bottom, that a great variety of fish in great numbers, are found. Eat, spawn, and be eaten are the rules governing this area. Marine life, large and small, is here in abundance to feast on the plentiful plant life, and food that falls or is washed onto the shelves.

DN

Migratory struggles

The details of spawning vary with the species of salmon. Indeed, the land-locked varieties do not migrate to sea. But the tenacity with which the spawning individuals will struggle to reach their spawning grounds is legendary. Salmon will often jump high waterfalls and overcome man-made obstacles in their heroic attempts to return to the stream of their birth and mate. The effort required to make leaps like this is tremendous – it takes a toll in terms of energy, weight loss, and injury. Some salmon arrive at the spawning ground half-dead, with their flesh hanging from their bones. Others cannot complete the journey and die without spawning.

sometimes travelling only a few miles, that too is a migration. In popular use, however, the word tends to be associated with longer trips, many of which display some inexplicable method of navigation.

Some migrations are adjustments to seasonal changes. Each spring, for example, as the waters warm northward, the Pacific pomfret swims from offshore near the southern tip of Vancouver Island to the Gulf of Alaska. The summer entry of bluefin tuna northward into Canadian waters as far as Notre Dame Bay in Newfoundland is another instance of a seasonally impelled migration.

Most migrations are made between feeding grounds and spawning grounds, and can be divided into three categories: (1) Migrations made within either salt or fresh water, as the case may be, without crossing the brackish barrier where they mix. (2) Migrations from salt back to fresh water in order to spawn. (3) Migrations from fresh back to salt water in order to spawn.

Migrations appear to be triggered by various conditions. Some respond to increases or decreases in temperatures. Some fishes seem to be impelled to migrate by changes in the photoperiod, that is, by lengthened or shortened days.

Migrations caused by seasonal changes are not necessarily the north/south swings we might expect. Indeed, to understand fish migration, and to grasp the tremendous variety of migratory patterns, it is first necessary to picture the massive upwellings, currents, stirrings, and settlings always going on in large bodies of water.

For the same reason that the rotation of the earth causes water to flow clockwise down a sink in our northern hemisphere, water tries to circulate clockwise in our oceans. Enormous vertical circulations also occur because the surface of water serves as a gigantic solar heat collector. As the sun's power declines in winter, surface layers cool, become more dense, and sink, especially at the poles. In the tropics, warm layers well up from the bottom. While all this is going on, predominant winds create huge drift currents across the surface.

Great rivers extend into the lakes and seas. Warm masses of water, surging up over continental shelves, sweep nutrients to the surface. Cold masses of water rush down the edge of the shelves. Boundaries are formed wherever these currents meet, limiting distribution of species according to temperature, salinity, depth, and available food. Finally, the boundaries themselves shift to and fro according to the weather, and the currents run in different directions at different depths and in different places.

Plankton, the myriad of floating microscopic plants and animals which make up the first link in the aquatic food chain, drift passively with these currents, forming what might be called 'portable pastures.' Their most prolific blooms occur along the continental shelves in temperate and tropical waters. This is where the action is for adult fishes, with smaller shoaling species like herring feeding on the plankton, and being in turn taken by the big predatory fishes like albacore.

However, the most favourable spawning grounds for most fishes are further inshore. Thus most species make an active migration back to the shore to spawn, while the young fry tend to drift away from shore to mature. Because different species prefer varying temperatures of water, some spawn inshore during winter, and others spawn inshore during summer.

Often, particularly in marine waters, a seasonal migration and spawning run will be one and the same. Atlantic mackerel winter in deep water along the edge of the continental shelf, from Sable Island south. In spring, they begin to move inshore and north, avoiding the Bay of Fundy where the water is usually too cold. They spawn in May, June, and early July in Canadian waters, most extensively in the southern Gulf of St Lawrence.

18 FAMOUS MIGRATIONS

Some of the most famous spawning migrations in the world are those made by salmon. Five species of Pacific salmon – chinook, coho, sockeye, pink, and chum – breast the currents of river systems from the Oregon coast to the Yukon River, sometimes travelling to the furthest freshets of the furthest lakes and tributaries to spawn in the clean gravel shoals.

Chinook travel the longest total distance. One recorded migration in salt water began near Adak Island, off Alaska, and entered the Columbia River system. Some venture as much as 1,000 miles out into the Pacific. In the Yukon River, some chinook travel over 1,800 miles upstream past the Alaska-Yukon border to spawn.

Chum also travel a long distance upstream, especially those entering the Yukon River, where they may swim almost 2,000 miles to Teslin Lake.

Sockeye spawning migrations almost invariably proceed up rivers with lakes in their systems, whereas coho will spawn in either the headwaters of large rivers, or shallow streams where the hookjawed males are often seen ending their migration in violent competition.

Most Pacific salmon begin their spawning migrations in fall, except for chinook, which enter spawning areas most of the year. However, chinook migrating into the rivers after the fall spawning period tend not to spawn until the following year, so that, generally, salmon are fall spawners.

Adult Pacific salmon, male and female, die after their spawning migration. Since the young fry do not hatch from their eggs until the following spring, Pacific salmon are said to be 'born orphans, who die childless.'

Atlantic salmon, which are more closely related to trouts and chars than to Pacific salmon, do not die after spawning. Atlantic salmon may undertake a return migration to the sea, and return once, perhaps even twice more to spawn.

It is believed that salmon return to the same tributary or stream in which they grew up; however, a few scientists have had difficulty in accepting this theory. Dr F. R. Harden Jones, who in 1968 published the first general, expert account of fish migration written in English since 1916, credits A. G. Huntsman, a former consulting director of the Fisheries Research Board of Canada, with an uncompromising and critical approach to the question that has prevented easy answers being accepted.

If Huntsman was a skeptic, another scientist working at the University of Rhode Island is playing a spoiler's role. Working with a computer, he has built up a mass of calculations which strongly suggest that salmon swim toward shore in random directions. Their numbers are so great, however, that enough of them will always hit their parent river to complete the spawning run.

Whatever one believes, or wants to believe, the truth about the salmon's homing ability is of great importance. Until it is clearly understood, practical measures for the conservation of salmon cannot likely be undertaken.

Other fishes migrate from salt to fresh water to spawn. The char, for instance, and the shad and the alewife, as well as the sea lamprey.

But eels migrate in the opposite direction, that is, from fresh water to salt. American eels are thought to spawn in the depths of the Sargasso Sea, which is roughly east of Florida and the Bahamas, and south of Bermuda.

Even this is an assumption, for its is based on the fact that larger and larger eel larvae are captured as one progresses away from the Sargasso Sea. No *adult* eels have ever been captured so far out at sea, however. V. D. Vladykov, another skeptical Canadian, suggests that the spawning ground for the American eel may be even further south.

It is known that the eel larvae drift northward with the Gulf Stream till they approach the coast. It takes about a year before they reach the continental shelf. Sometime after this they undergo a metamorphosis, and become elvers or glass eels. Finally, in the spring, they enter estuaries and fresh-water streams from the Gulf of Mexico to southern Greenland. Many turn into the Gulf of St Lawrence and swim up the St Lawrence and into Lake Ontario, from which a few enter into Lake Erie through the Welland Canal.

American eels stay in fresh water from five to ten years, although individuals as old as twenty years have been reported. Finally, on some dark night between late August and mid-November, they begin moving downstream on their long run back to their presumed spawning grounds in the Sargasso Sea where, it is further presumed, they die, for no mature spawned-out eels have ever been caught returning to fresh water.

Common or American eels in the elver stage.

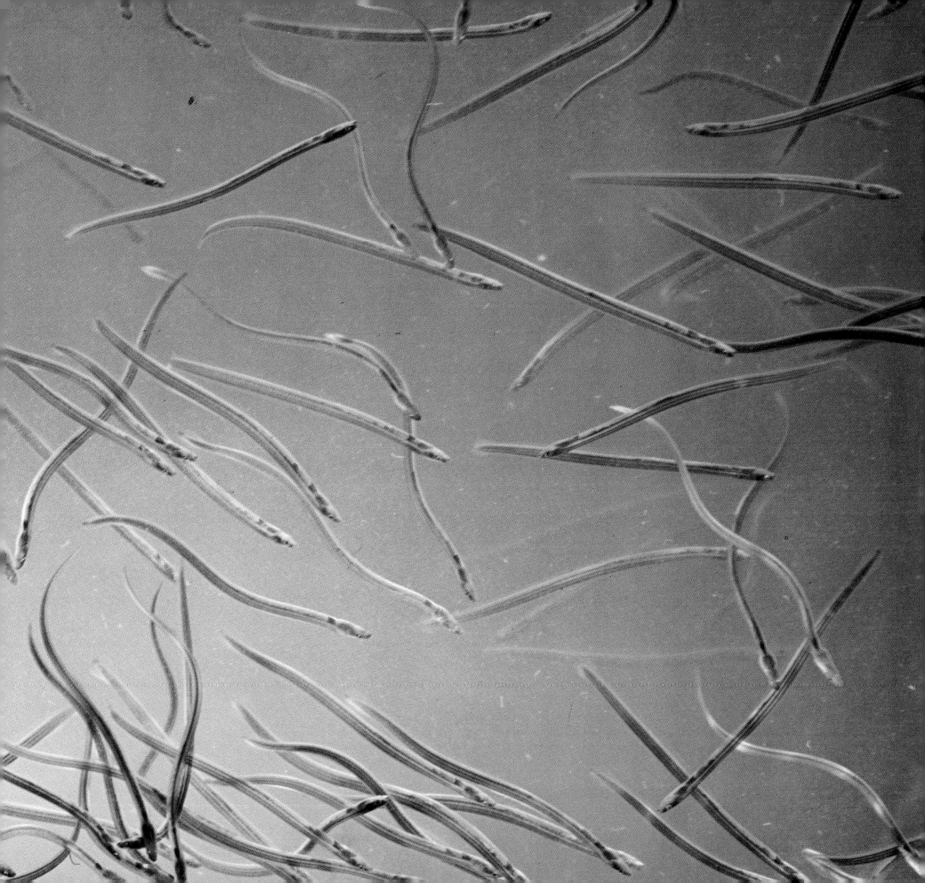

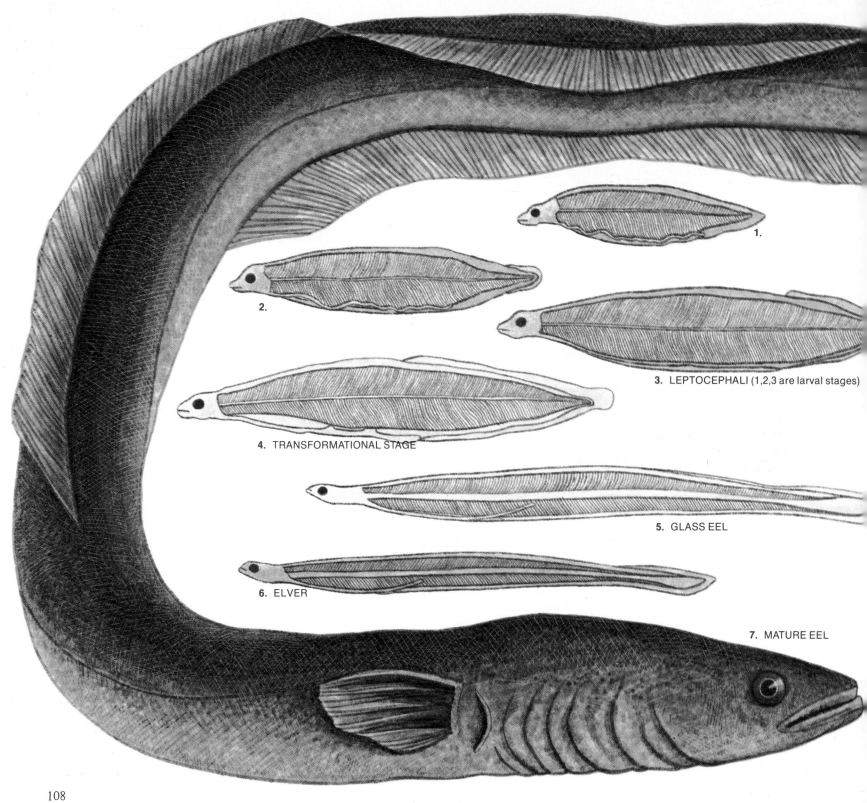

1.

2.

3. LEPTOCEPHALI (1,2,3 are larval stages)

4. TRANSFORMATIONAL STAGE

5. GLASS EEL

6. ELVER

7. MATURE EEL

108

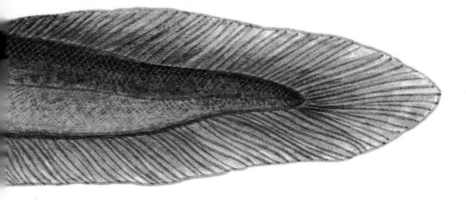

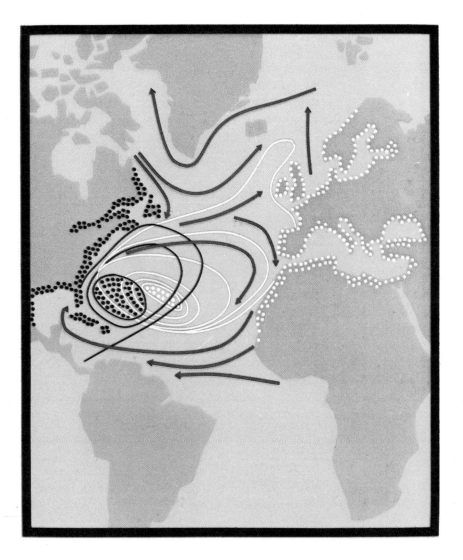

The mysteries of eel migration

Unlike the salmon, the American eel migrates from fresh to salt water to spawn. The eel begins life in the clear waters of the Sargasso Sea. Wafted on the strong currents of the Gulf Stream and Florida current, the young find their way back to stream entrances, where they shrink into tiny strings called elvers, and make their way, feeding voraciously, into the lakes and rivers of the Great Lakes drainages. As adults, they may grow to over three feet long, and are aggressive predators in fresh waters in Quebec and Ontario. At seven to ten years, the adults leave these waters to retrace the path they travelled as young eels. The path is slightly different, and they pick up the southbound remnants of the Labrador Current which they ride into the deep waters under the Gulf Stream and eventually back to the spawning grounds. Part of the answer to the mystery of this incredible migration lies in the eel's ability to detect minute electrical differences which occur in the ocean as a result of currents of water sliding past each other.

19 HOMING INSTINCTS

Proof of fishes' navigational ability and the inclination to home is most striking, however. Pacific tidepool sculpins try to return to their home pool if moved. Fishes have been observed navigating according to visual landmarks when they can see the bottom. Coastal species memorize the deeper depressions during incoming tides. When tides go out, they quickly find the route back via the depressions.

This capability was demonstrated in a series of experiments carried out in 1960 by Lester Aronson of the American Museum of Natural History. At flood tide, he and assistants hollowed out depressions not far from shore. Several species of fish were caught in the depressions during the next ebb tide, but they merely jumped from pool to pool to the water. One fish covered ten yards through eleven pools over a zig zag course.

At the next ebb tide, the group kept a fish prisoner in the pool furthest from open water for a short time after the tide had retreated. Meanwhile, the next pool was filled with sand. When the fish was released, it jumped onto the dry spot where the pool should have been.

F. Buckland's theory about fishes' ability to navigate according to smells is also alive and well. Fishes do have a keen sense of smell. Bear paws and other odour-producing agents placed in water upstream from migrating salmon make them retreat downstream. Experiments in which fishes' nostrils were plugged show that this interferes with navigational ability.

Sockeye were once taken from the outlet of Great Central Lake on Vancouver Island, and from Sweltzer Creek on the Fraser River, and confined to tanks. When water from their home stream was dropped into the tanks, the fish dispersed and began swimming faster, but there was no similar response when water from another stream was added.

If currents can carry or guide young toward nursery and feeding grounds, it may be possible, goes another theory, for fishes to use currents as a means of navigating back to their spawning area. The process enabling this is thought to involve the lateral line, a sixth sense peculiar to fishes, which can be seen in most species in a line of specially shaped scales along the sides. The sense organs attached to the lateral line are thought to be supersensitive to pressure. By equalizing pressure on either side, fishes are able to swim against the strongest flow in a current.

This does not explain how salmon might be able to migrate back from the seemingly trackless ocean to a coastal estuary with any accuracy; but remember that the ocean is not trackless. There are undoubtedly many currents at sea as yet undiscovered that fishes may follow. Furthermore, they might be guided by gradients in temperature or salinity where different masses of water meet. Maybe the ability to follow such clues works together with other senses such as smell or sight.

Some fishes may orient themselves according to the sun. In one confirmation of this possibility, A. D. Hasler and co-workers put a bluegill, a member of the sunfish family, into a radially divided tank. During the day, under open sky, the fish learned to seek out the most northern compartment. Under overcast conditions, it was not able to make a correct choice.

Further experiments of this nature were carried out by W. Braemer. He trained fish to seek the northern compartment at different times of the day, and began artificially altering the cycle between night and day to upset the fish's internal time clock.

This means that, on a given day at a given time, the sun would *appear* to be at a different point in the sky. Nevertheless the fish was still able to find its way to the correct compartment, proving that some species can correct for changes in the sun's azimuth. Other experiments by W. E. Johnson and C. Groot on smolts of sockeye in Babine Lake, British Columbia, suggest that the smolts use a similar kind of celestial reckoning to find their way out of the lake.

There is also laboratory evidence indicating that scales of fishes are sensitive to minute changes in electromagnetic waves. In nature, this would evidently make them equally sensitive to the earth's magnetic field. Thus the scales may act as navigational sensors, enabling fishes to zero in on the correct direction during migration.

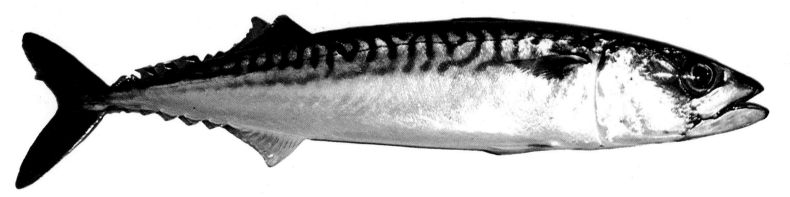

The lack of an air bladder forces mackerel (above) *and some other fishes to swim constantly to keep afloat and to obtain oxygen.*

20 HAZARDOUS JOURNEYS

The effort expended during migration depends on the distance travelled, the hazards encountered, and how well the fish is adapted for the task. The Pacific sea lamprey swims against the downstream current in spurts, and rests in between by merely sucking rocks. In the final thrusts upstream, the flesh of chinook salmon may literally hang from the bones. Eels stick close to shore, where the current will least affect them.

One adaptation that likely assists in long migrations is an air bladder which inflates or deflates as certain fishes change depth. This means the fish remains in a state of buoyancy, and it can therefore concentrate its energy on swimming forward.

But species like the shark and mackerel have no such organ, and, being naturally heavier than water, must spend energy not only in swimming forward, but to keep from sinking. It has always puzzled experts that they can still swim so efficiently.

A new theory announced in 1973 by a scientist at Cambridge suggests that they swim upward, and then turn down into long "glides" much the same way hawks and eagles do when migrating. Calculations reportedly show that this trick would result in a 50 per cent energy-saving over a given distance.

Migrating fishes are always potential meals for other species, or larger members of their own species who may be cannibalistic. In the marine environment, the food chain progresses up to the great whales, and, finally, to man, with his long lines and seines, drift nets and trawls. In fresh waters it builds to osprey, otter, bear, and once again culminates in man, with his rods and spears and weirs.

Hydro-electric dams create problems in both upstream and downstream journeys. On smaller dams, a series of pools, each about a foot higher than the last, form a fishway up the side of the dam. On big, multi-million dollar dams, a complicated collection system is built across the face of the dam. On Nova Scotia's East River, Atlantic salmon proceeding upstream are collected in a tank and trucked around three major dams.

During downstream migration, some young may be killed when passing through hydro turbines. This resulted in a kill-off of 10 to 15 per cent of salmon smolts at dams on the East River before special louvers were installed to direct the smolts away from the turbines. In Ontario, adult American eels heading back to sea descend through the turbines of a dam near Cornwall. Enough are sometimes killed so as to interfere with turbine maintenance, perhaps giving grim satisfaction to the god of the eels.

Speed during migration varies. Some fishes drift passively with currents, particularly when moving as young to nursery and feeding grounds. The Pacific soupfin shark, which appears to move north along the coast as far as Hecate Strait,

Obstacles and barriers

Salmon encounter numerous barriers on their spawning runs, including large hydro-electric dams (above), small logging dams (right), waterfalls, rapids, flooding, pollution, predators, and fishermen. Some prove insurmountable, and although the fish try valiantly, they cannot get through and are doomed to die without spawning.

Man-made aids are sometimes available to help fish get by obstacles. Some hydro-electric dams have a series of pools, each about a foot higher than the last, which form fish ladders up the side of the dam. Large dams sometimes have a complicated collection system built across the face of the dam. In some instances, salmon are collected in tanks and trucked around large dams.

These same barriers present problems for the young when they are migrating back downstream. They are frequently killed if trapped in turbines at hydro dams. Special louvers to direct smolts away from turbines help reduce this problem.

112

can move at sustained speeds of ten miles per day for up to 1,000 miles. Sockeye salmon proceed upriver at about thirty miles per day. American shad cover up to fifty miles per day.

Spawning migrations, even the long ones, frequently coincide with fasts. As Pacific herring approach the coast to spawn in autumn, feeding comes to a stop, and their gonads mature till they make up to 20 per cent of body weight. None of the Pacific salmon feed after entering fresh waters. During this trip, sockeye salmon use over 90 per cent of their fat, and over 33 per cent of their protein reserves, depending on the distance to spawning beds.

Such fine tuning of energy reserves to far-off goals shows how dangerous delays to migration may be, and why a fishway around a dam may be a compromise between the 'need' to produce electricity and to perpetuate the survival of a commercially important fish at the same time.

21 MIGRATORY ADAPTATIONS

Various physical transformations may also take place prior to, or during, a spawning migration. Male Atlantic salmon develop a pronounced hook on the lower jaw and the head becomes elongated. The larval form of the American eel when it is drifting from the Sargasso Sea is pale, almost transparent, flat and leaf-like in shape. It has sharp teeth, and grows to about three inches. As it prepares to enter the estuaries and marshes, it shrinks to about two inches, loses its teeth, and becomes what is known as a glass eel: a translucent forecast of the mature eel shape. Only when it finally enters fresh water does it become dark-coloured.

The adaptation permitting passage through the brackish boundary between salt and fresh water is one of the most fascinating aspects of migration. Its purpose is to balance the fish's concentration of salts in the blood and body fluids with the degree of salts in the enveloping water.

As the fish moves across the salt/freshwater zone, its skin, which is semi-permeable, allows water to pass from one side to the other. A certain amount of salts are transferred as well,

The spawning of the kokanee

Freshwater populations of sockeye salmon, called kokanee salmon, spawn during the fall. Although they are not noted for extended migrations as are their anadromous relatives, they do exhibit the same startling colour transformations and ritualized behaviour. When it enters the gravel bed or stream inlet that is its spawning ground, the mature kokanee is striking red-orange colour (far left). *The breeding male* (above left) *appears to be slightly deformed, with its humped back, turned up snout, and gaping teeth.*

The nest is prepared by the female who rolls on her side and beats her tail up and down, flailing the gravel. Once on the spawning gravel (below left), *the male and female swim to the nest and deposit their eggs and sperm. After the spawning, the female covers the nest with gravel. She may then go on to other nesting spots and spawn with other males. Hundreds of orange eggs are laid by each female.*

Under the gravel, the eggs are safe. Although they may be disturbed by later spawning salmon or erosion, most of them will remain until they hatch some months later. When they emerge from the gravel in the spring, the young will be free-swimming fry. Within the next year, they will attain a length of from five to fifteen inches.

Kokanee inhabit the middle layers of open lakes where they feed on plankton and bottom organisms. The young are preyed upon by a variety of other fishes, including rainbow trout and coho salmon. At maturity they, too, will spawn, undergoing the last transformation that precedes their death.

After spawning, the adult kokanee of both sexes die within a few days to several weeks. The male kokanee (overleaf), *although still alive, is in the process of decomposing.*

The kokanee, basically a sea fish, must expend energy constantly to maintain a balance of its body salts in fresh water. Gills and kidneys are the prime organs used by salmon to make the adjustments necessary to move from fresh to salt water and

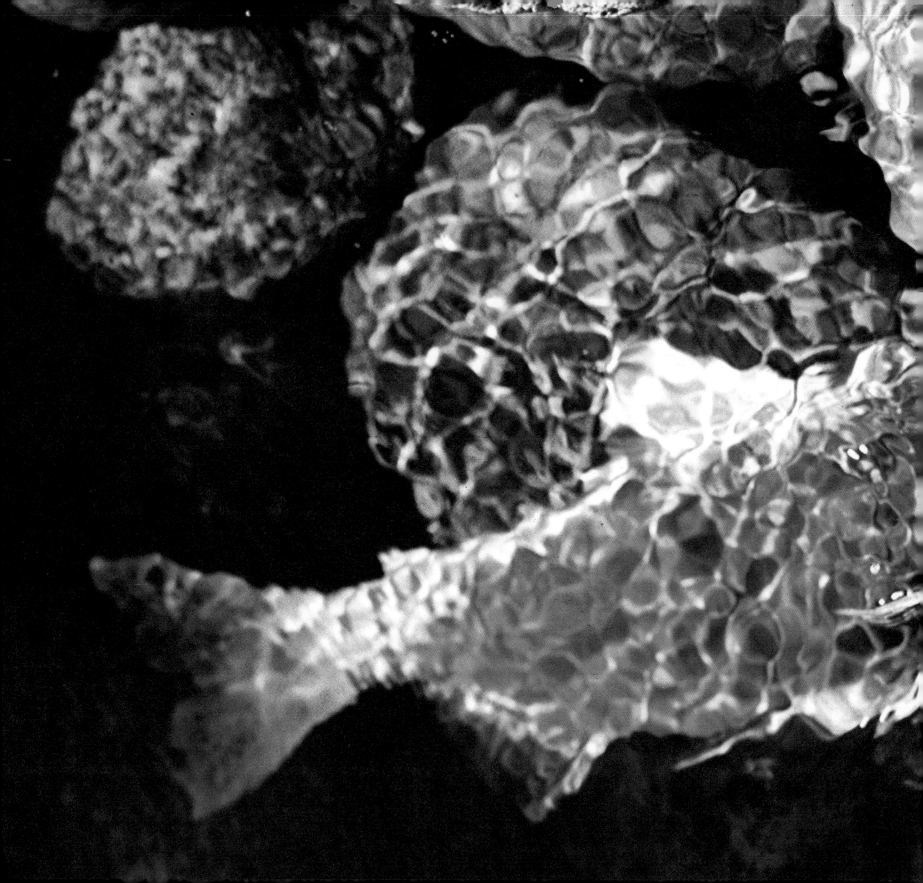

from salt to fresh. Gill filaments (above) are normally gorged with blood, since they are the body's means of oxygenating blood. Specialized cells in the gills called chloride cells take up or secrete salt ions to allow the fish to adjust to the water in which it finds itself. Young, anadromous salmon, going from fresh to salt water, make this transition easily.

During spawning, when so much energy is spent for migration and production of reproductive material, the salmon cannot also maintain the balance of body salts. As a result, the tissues of the fish become saturated with fresh water – a potentially lethal situation.

After spawning, most salmon are unable to correct this balance and to re-establish an osmotic equilibrium, and they therefore die. The Atlantic salmon are able to survive this state and will return to the sea, spawning two or three times during their lifetimes, whereas the Pacific salmon generally die after spawning once.

117

but in the opposite direction. The dilute water passes toward the more saturated, and the more concentrated salts pass to the less concentrated. This exchange is more pronounced through the thin membranes of the gills and mouth.

If this were all that occurred, however, the fish could lose so much body water while moving from fresh to salt water that its tissues would eventually shrivel up. And in swimming the opposite direction, from salt to fresh water, it could take on too much water and become waterlogged.

Therefore the voiding organs perform specific and different functions under each condition. In salt water, the fish must retain water in its tissues. It therefore must swallow great quantities of water. The little waste that is produced is highly concentrated with salts.

In fresh water, the problem is to retain salt and to keep water out of the tissues. Here, equally great quantities of water are swallowed. The water passes through, producing large amounts of waste with dilute concentrations of salt.

The time taken for this process to bring about a state of balance varies with the species. Fishes like the flounders, which commonly spend a good deal of time in brackish water, may make the adjustment rapidly, from within minutes up to twenty-four hours. A sea-run trout accomplishes it in about eighty to 170 hours, and salmon smolts need at least 200 hours.

---

22 THE SEARCH FOR ANSWERS

Knowledge of fish migration has been painstakingly pieced together, mostly with data gathered by tagging or marking. Probably the earliest record of tagging occurred in Sweden in the fifteenth century, when a pike was taken from a pond with a ring around its neck saying it had been put there by Frederick the Second. Skeptics, however, claimed the fish was a fake put together with the bones from smaller fishes.

Scientific tagging is usually said to have begun when an Italian zoologist began studying hooks found in the mouths of bluefin tuna. Bluefin caught in the Mediterranean had Portugese hooks from the Azores. Others taken off the coast of Spain had hooks from Norway. A link between bluefin on our side of the Atlantic and the old world was established when one was caught off the coast of Sardinia with a hook in its flesh that was made in Akron, Ohio. The bluefin has subsequently entered the top ranks of known long-distance migrants.

Tagging and marking is a laborious task. Fishes produce a mucous on their skin which, as is well known, makes them rather slippery. Yet they must be handled with great care, for wounds, abrasions, and serious loss of scales easily occur.

Imagine, for instance, the effort involved in marking 64,500 delicate sockeye fingerlings for an experiment carried out in 1950 at Quesnel Lake, British Columbia. The project ended with only 227 recoveries of marked fish, which indicates clearly the massive work required to counter the odds against recovery.

Some species like cod do not have an opening in their air bladder which acts as a safety valve to let excess gas out when the fish is brought up from the depths for tagging. Their air bladder almost invariably explodes.

Devising a mark or tag that will not harm the fish but which will be detected by a fisherman, plant worker, or automatic machine has tested the ingenuity of scientists, indeed. Nearly seventy different tags are officially listed as tried. The most popular is thought to be the Peterson method, which involves attaching two tags to the bony gill covering, much like a pair of cuff links.

Marking is usually a form of benign mutilation in which a fin is clipped. Tattooing has been tried, but the marks fade after a few weeks. Harmless radioisotopes which can be detected in fish processing plants have been used. Even parasites have been infected into stocks of Pacific salmon so catches at sea reveal the fish's origin, as well as how extensively its stock mixes with other populations.

Bugging with sonic transmitters is already used a great deal, and many more applications are in store. The smallest transmitter at present is a cylindrical capsule one and three-eighths of an inch long by three-eighths of an inch in diameter with an operating life of two days and a signal range of a quarter mile.

Fish tagging

The method of tracing movements of fishes by tagging or marking them has given rise to a line of research which has become of immense importance.

Useful, and often unexpected, facts are revealed when tag returns are analyzed. The length of a fish is usually noted when it is tagged; when it is recaptured, scientists are able to measure its growth rate. Information on the death rate of a species, migration patterns, and many other points on which we have scant knowledge is being garnered by biologists all over the world from tag returns.

Many early attempts at fish tagging were not particularly successful, since a tag which would stay on a fish, but not harm or kill it, was difficult to develop. Today, such advanced forms as sonic transmitters (below), which are inserted internally, are being developed by many nations, and point the way to the possibility of learning much more detail about fishes daily habits and their ways of life than ever before.

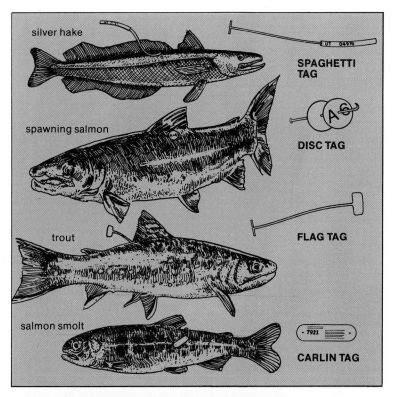

silver hake — SPAGHETTI TAG

spawning salmon — DISC TAG

trout — FLAG TAG

salmon smolt — CARLIN TAG

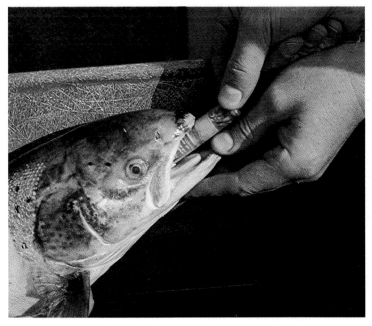

The fishery biologists catching and tagging smallmouth bass must ascertain that the fish they are tagging are healthy, normal members of their species. They exercise great care not to damage scales or fins or rub off the protective mucous coating, which can invite disease. Many hundreds must be tagged in order for an appreciable number to be caught and turned in.

The tagging of smallmouth bass is done with the aid of an anaesthetic and sterile needles. Their eventual recovery may give scientists new information on growth and mortality rates, migration and population numbers.

With sonic bugging, it is possible to monitor not only the fish's destination, but where is lingers, and where it swims quickly forward. Some monitoring involves continuous tracking from a boat. In other instances, electronic gates in narrow passages register crossings.

Data on the depth at which fishes may be swimming, which scientists have lacked for some time, may at last be available thanks to another new transmitter developed by the Biological Station of the Fisheries Research Board at St Andrews, New Brunswick, and the University of New Brunswick.

Multi-channel transmitters are also now on their way which will enable researchers to study several factors simultaneously, such as swimming speed, salinity, temperature, heartbeat, gill rate, etc.

Recovery, of course, is what most marking and tagging is all about. One problem is to motivate fishermen and workers to watch for these special fish, and to report them.

Lotteries have been used in Norway and the United States, and a research program begun in 1972 on salmon in Georgia Strait offers three dollars to anyone turning in one of 400,000 cohoe and 2.5 million chinook which have had their adipose fins removed. Each fish has a hair-thin tag inserted in its nose with magnetic coded information on it which will be decoded by the Fisheries Research Board. To further stimulate returns, each name is entered in one of sixteen $100 draws.

There is no clear-cut answer to the origin of fish migration. One theory holds that it evolved because there may not be enough food and space in spawning grounds to maintain both young and adult. All of our important commercial species of fish are commercial not only because we have found pleasant ways to cook them, but because they are abundant.

Such species – cod, smelt, bluefin, salmon, for instance – tend to be highly migratory. This would mean that migration is a natural step towards ensuring survival through abundance. If the parent had succeeded because it was spawned in a favourable environment, it would likely strive to return to that environment to ensure success of its young in turn.

If some individuals were driven into other territories, from salt to fresh waters, or from fresh to salt waters, seasonal changes may have caused them to turn back, and return again, until a rhythm became fixed.

Knowledge about fish migration continues to lag behind that of bird migration because water, after all, is not an environment fit for man. We do not share it with fishes as we share the earth and air with mammals and birds. Because the activities of fishes are so less evident, they are of less interest to the average person.

Research has thus been left to the scientists, who tend to direct their comments to each other rather than to the public. Icthyology has no legion of naturalists deployed in the depths with notepad and camera, ready to gather evidence, as they do in the field for ornithology.

Some information may be gathered from fishermen, but, as F. R. Harden Jones says, 'One is likely to learn more about the movements of boats than the movement of fish.' Still, it was anglers who argued for years that the wind must blow hard for at least a day or more before lake trout in Simcoe Lake, Ontario, will enter the shoals to spawn. A six-year study by the Canadian Department of Fisheries finally concluded the theory was largely correct.

The increasing popularity of SCUBA diving may eventually put the equivalent of the field naturalist into the water. Divers have already shown that the longfin sculpin was seldom taken in Juan de Fuca Strait and the Strait of Georgia because it frequently hangs vertically on rock faces. It is hoped that such people will be interested in the behaviour of fishes in and for itself, rather than to the end 'utilization' as it is called in so many studies.

WAYNE MCLAREN

The mysteries surrounding fishes and their activities in their natural habitat are being explored today as never before, with the increasing use of underwater photography and diving.

PART FIVE
THREATS TO OUR WATERS

Until man became truly adept at destroying the world around him, the homely codfish was one of this country's most abundant natural resources. As long ago as 1497, John Cabot sailed home to tell an astonished England of how he had dipped cod by the basketful from the waters around 'New Found Land.' Cod fisheries later became one of the mainstays of pioneer Canada.

During the 1930s, when nearly everything was scarce, boxcars of dried cod were shipped to us drought-ridden prairie-dwellers, and although the great salty slabs were too strong for my youthful palate, I was as impressed as Cabot. Clearly, nothing – not even the awful Depression – could diminish the bounty of Canada's seas.

I was wrong. Gus Etchegary, vice-president of a Newfoundland fishing firm and president of the Save our Fisheries Association, recently told a sorrowful tale to a St John's

Like most pelagic fish, the capelin normally travel in schools. They are preyed on by codfish, and are themselves the subject of an intensive fishing industry.

service club. Huge foreign fishing fleets are ravaging the cod off the coast of Labrador between January and May each year, he said. This being the spawning season, the decks of some vessels become ankle deep in spawn, which is hosed over the sides. As a result, fewer and fewer fish are left, or are born to migrate to inshore waters, and the cod catch off northeast Newfoundland has dropped alarmingly.

The cod is only one aquatic victim of man's arrogance and carelessness. For centuries we have assumed that the fish of this world are infinite and that the waters of this world can cope with anything we dump into them. Consequently, some fish are now extinct, other species are in peril, rivers and lakes are dying, and the oceans are becoming a gigantic cesspool. We are dangerously close to fishing the world's waters empty. Failing that, we will simply poison them. Jacques Cousteau, whose undersea sagas are familiar to every television viewer, has warned that unless ocean pollution is stopped it will put an end to most forms of life in the seas within fifty years.

We have been slow to grasp the magnitude of the problem. The excellent *Red Data Book* – official catalogue of endangered creatures around the world, published by the Inter-

The cod (above) *was once an extremely abundant species. The Atlantic salmon* (right) *is threatened by fishing and pollution, and by man-made obstacles that impede their spawning runs.*

national Union for Conservation of Nature and Natural Resources – devotes 300 pages to beleaguered animals and birds but a mere fourteen to fish. Fish are every bit as much in danger and the IUCN is concerned with all creatures. But those of land and air can be studied with relative ease and counted fairly accurately throughout their life cycles. Getting into the fishes' habitat is more difficult, and population counts are partly guesswork.

Nevertheless, we know that in and around Canada alone, many fish populations have been done grievous and perhaps irreparable harm. Dr D. E. McAllister, curator of fishes at the National Museum of Natural Sciences in Ottawa, cites twenty-eight 'rare, endangered, or possibly extinct' species, from the Pacific sardine to the Atlantic whitefish. And his list does not include such threatened species as the cod, redfish, haddock, herring, or Atlantic salmon.

The source of the onslaught is easily traced: an ever-increasing population of greedy indifferent humans. By far the biggest threats are overfishing and pollution. Both are controllable, but both require human understanding and stiff, well-enforced laws, frequently at the international level. Considering the world's past achievements in other international affairs, the future looks bleak for the fish.

As the world's population soars and hunger becomes a global concern, fish offer an increasingly valuable high-protein food. The world's fishing fleets pull in about 70 million metric tons per year, more than double the catch of 1958. Peru (with a huge offshore anchovy fishery), Japan (which sends fleets into every ocean), Red China, and Russia lead the catch.

Scientists meanwhile are seeking more effective ways to use fish. One is by turning it into meal or flour. Not only does this use every bit of a fish but it utilizes less-desirable species that get into commercial nets and in the past have been tossed away. The United States has developed FPC (fish protein concentrate) which transforms everything, including scales and entrails, into an odourless, pure, protein-rich white powder. It can be stirred into any food or mixed with flour. With it, the world's animal-protein needs could be supplied for less than a cent per person per day – *if* the fish supply holds out.

But will it? Some biologists see it lasting twenty years. The Food and Agriculture Organization of the United Nations offers a bleaker prospect: at the present rate of catch, which could increase by three or four million tons per year, we may reach the 'practical' harvest limit – 85 million tons per year – in the 1970s.

A few decades ago, commercial fishing was a relatively simple operation, and fish populations could easily stay ahead of the catch. Since the Second World War, however, and partly with technology learned during that war, fishing has become a science and a massive industry. Consider the $2.5 million air-conditioned U.S. tuna seiner, *Captain Vincent Gann*: its net is nearly a mile long and 300 feet deep, and it can take 250 tons of tuna in a sweep. It, in turn, pales beside the factory ships of Russia and Japan. One such is the Soviet's *Boevaya Slava* (*Battle Glory*), as big as a city block. Fitted out like a land-based fish factory, it stays at sea for months while two dozen catcher ships feed it with fish.

Such fleets can zero in unerringly on whole schools of fish that once lay unseen. Aircraft sometimes aid in the spotting.

Echo sounders locate fish lying on the bottom. And if any of them are still hiding out, they won't be safe for long: some ships will be equipped with computers coupled to underwater television cameras which will spot the fish and set nets at the proper level.

23 MANAGEMENT FOR CONSERVATION

Although this methodical pillage worries conservationists the world over, it is of particular concern to Canada, which has one of the largest coastlines on its three oceans and one of the largest areas of continental shelf. The ocean depths are a wasteland, in terms of fish population. By far the bulk of the world's fisheries lie off the shores of the continents no deeper than 1200 feet. Here, on the shelves, luxuriating among plants and small marine creatures, the fish feed and flourish. And here, naturally, come the factory fleets. Newfoundland Premier Frank Moores has estimated that foreigners catch nine of every ten fish netted within 200 miles of Canada's shores.

Overfishing has made the haddock of New England and eastern Canada an endangered species. Gus Etchegary of St John's reports that between 1955 and 1960 haddock represented 70 per cent of the total landings of Newfoundland's deep-sea trawler fleet. Now the haddock catch is no longer even a statistic in the region.

The same thing is happening to redfish. Yellow flounder are dwindling. At the present catch rate, the tuna is probably doomed. Less than 10 per cent of Atlantic herring are left. Herring, being a favourite food of cod, mackerel, and other larger fish, are an essential link in the marine ecosystem. Even the capelin—a tiny silvery fish much favoured by Newfound-

Government research vessels (left) *are normally much smaller than fishing ships. The Russian five-ton trawler* (top) *is capable of gathering in thousands of pounds of fish in a single haul. The fish-tracking equipment* (centre and bottom) *homes in on schools of fish.*

landers for food, fertilizer, and bait – was being swept into Norwegian and Russian factory ships in 1973.

One of the hottest issues for Canadians in the early 1970s was the plight of the Atlantic salmon. In 1972 federal Environment Minister Jack Davis personally rated it as endangered. Canada's total commercial catch the previous year was down to about 4 million pounds, from 6.3 million in 1967. In the same period, the total catch from three New Brunswick rivers, the St John, Restigouche, and Miramichi, went from 126,324 fish to 26,225 per year – a drop of 80 per cent.

As an anadromous fish (meaning it lives in both salt and fresh water), the salmon is subjected to every kind of abuse. Inland, hydro-electric dams interfere with its spawning runs, while towns and factories spew sewage and chemical wastes into its habitat.

For centuries the salmon could at least flee from man during the part of its life cycle spent at sea. Then, in the early 1960s, the U.S. nuclear submarine *Nautilus* happened on to a great Atlantic salmon feeding ground off the coast of Greenland. Through fish-tagging, Canadians know that many of those salmon come from Canadian waters. Danish fishing fleets moved in with a vengeance, and the salmon count in parts of eastern Canada has dwindled ever since. After long and heated wrangles, Canada wrung a promise from the Danes to stop high seas' salmon fishing in 1976.

Meanwhile, commercial fishing on the St John, Restigouche, and Miramichi rivers, and off Port-aux-Basques on the southwestern tip of Newfoundland was banned until at least 1978. These four areas have accounted for roughly 25 per cent of the total Canadian catch, and the fishermen involved are being compensated at a cost of several million dollars to the Canadian taxpayer.

Since overfishing in international waters can be curbed only on a worldwide basis, the third United Nations Law of the Sea Conference, scheduled for the summer of 1974 in Caracas, Venezuela, was billed as 'the most important lawmaking conference ever held.' Its agenda included pollution, mineral resources, fishing and navigation rights, and territorial limits.

In simpler times, the territorial waters of nations were mostly established three miles offshore – about as far as a cannon could fire. In 1970 Canada extended her territorial

sea to the twelve-mile limit. But with the persistent rape of the coastal shelf, this country began lobbying for jurisdiction over coastal waters for 200 miles out (some South American countries have already set such a precedent) *and* to the outer margin of the shelf. In Canada's case, this would extend jurisdiction from 400 to 600 miles into the Atlantic at certain points.

The object of this was not exclusive claim to the fish in those waters but to management control for conservation purposes. Biologists now know that many species of coastal fish, often miles out to sea, rely upon the nutrients from inland rivers and bays. Good management of fisheries and waters within, say, eastern Canada is therefore important to marine life far out into the Atlantic coastal shelf. The responsibility of any coastal nation to protect environmental quality should be balanced by authority to manage, Canada reasons. This, of course, is unpopular with countries that sponsor the roaming predator fleets. Yet regulation is essential. Already there have been clashes at sea, and some South American countries patrol their waters with gunboats.

Equally unpopular with entrepreneurs is the possibility of restrictions on mining of the ocean floor. At least forty companies from different countries have invested small fortunes in preparation for undersea mining. One American firm promised its shareholders a million tons of production by 1975. The Howard Hughes organization reportedly has invested $250 million in 'nodule' mining. Nodules, ranging from pebbles to boulders, are strewn over the ocean beds, bearing rich deposits of iron, copper, manganese, cobalt, and nickel. Producing them could drastically alter the price and power structure of the world's conventional mineral holdings.

Management of fisheries and mining may come nevertheless, with laws and cooperation at the international level, if enough sane governments lend their support. Pollution control of the seas is much more difficult to achieve. Companies with a conscience already insist that their ocean vessels obey

The once great schools of herring are fast dwindling since about 1964 as a result of enormous fish catches being made off Canada's coasts.

anti-pollution rules, such as flushing bilges into dock-side holding basins and retaining garbage for disposal in port. But many independent shippers continue to use the sea as a septic tank. What's the harm of a few more garbage bags or gallons of oily waste, they reason? And who's to know?

As yet, there is no effective way to police the ocean litterers, and an estimated two million tons of oil are dumped at sea every year. Oil-burning vessels fill the air with additional tons, in the form of smut. It's believed that there are now traces of oil everywhere in the oceans of the world. Adventurer Thor Heyerdahl told of seeing lumps of solidified oil (not to mention plastic bottles) floating in mid-Atlantic.

Nor is oil the only contaminant. In 1973, the Japanese Ministry of Health and Welfare warned that nation to reduce sharply its consumption of locally caught fish because nearly all coastal waters were contaminated by mercury, cadmium, copper, and other chemicals. At about the same time, the University of California Radioactive Research Centre reported that nuclear fallout can be detected in any fifty-gallon sample of sea water. And the human agonies of the Viet Nam war overshadowed another ugly aftermath: shellfish and finfish in Vietnamese rivers and coastal waters may be contaminated with dioxin, a component of the defoliant 2,4,5-T that American forces dropped by the ton on forests to destroy enemy ground cover.

---

24 INLAND POLLUTION

Control of inland pollution is at least within reach of each individual country (excluding luckless Viet Nam), but Canada, for one, is a long way from perfect purity. Offenders are everywhere. Farmers allow their cows to wade in streams and

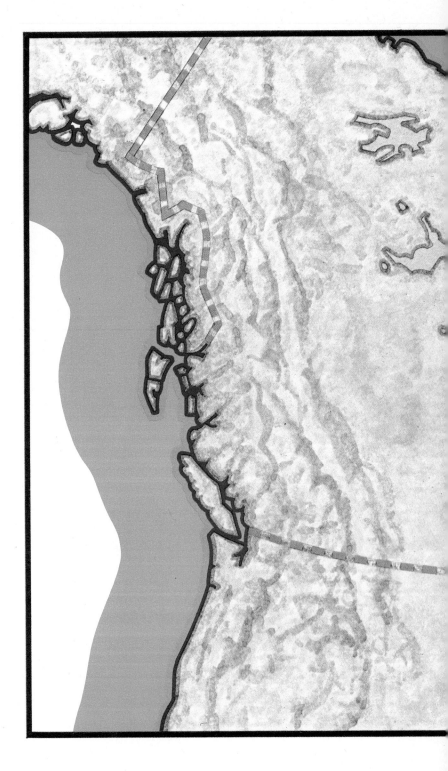

This map shows the original three-mile fishing limit, today's twelve-mile limit, and the proposed territorial boundary of up to 200 miles, which conservationists hope would aid in preserving endangered species.

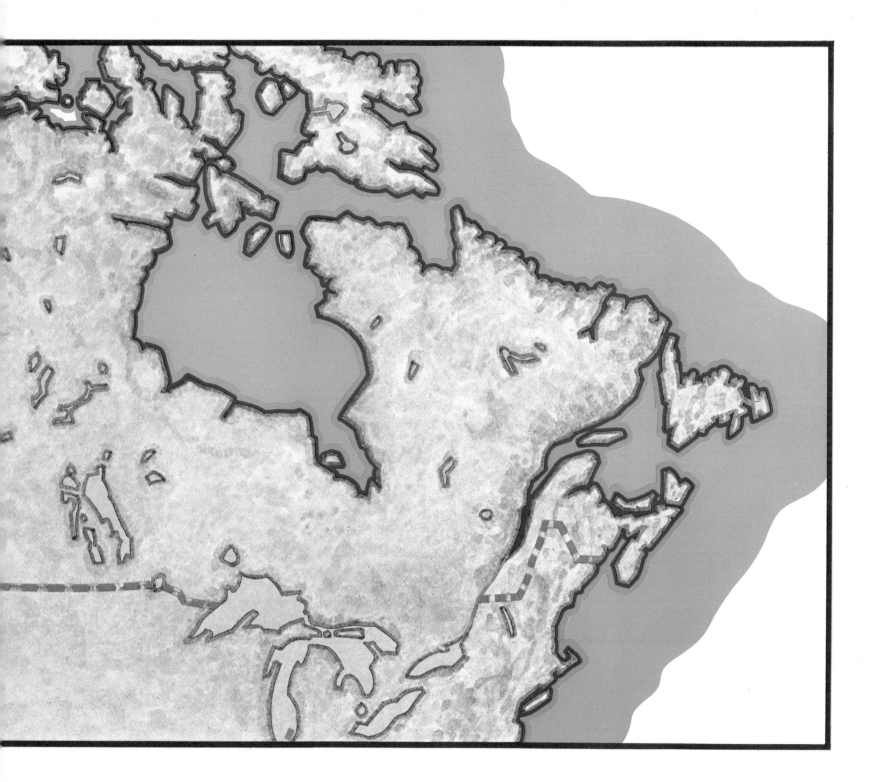

foul them, and they chop down trees to every water's edge instead of leaving a swath of growth to prevent erosion. Fruit growers spray pesticides indiscriminately. Cottagers dump wastes into the lakes.

Most municipal sewage systems in Canada lack all but the very rudimentary treatment facilities. As a result they release fertilizing elements into the waters, causing a build-up of plant growth. Called *eutrophication*, it coats beaches with slime and weeds and drains oxygen from the waters – oxygen that fish need for survival. The average Canadian contributes about three pounds of phosphorus and a dozen pounds of nitrogen to sewage every year, enough to create a half-ton of living plant tissue. Yet our village and city fathers continue to ignore the need for better sanitation.

The greatest polluters are industries, and paper companies are among the worst, says Dr McAllister of the National Museum of Natural Sciences. Wood fibres from their plants form a mat on the bottom of rivers which may extend for miles, preventing normal growth of bottom fauna. At one time, paper mills also used mercury compounds to desludge their pipes. Mercury compounds accumulate in fish to the extent that they are sometimes unfit for human consumption. Predators such as pike, pickerel, goldeye, and swordfish are particularly susceptible: mercury gets into small marine creatures, which are eaten by smaller fish, which are eaten by bigger ones, with a cumulative build-up of the poison.

Paper makers are not, however, the only culprits. Lakes around Sudbury were 'knocked out' long ago by smelting operations, says McAllister, and the effects are spreading. Scores of other industries discharge heated waters, from cooling systems, into rivers and lakes. Many species in the aquatic food chain are highly sensitive to changes in temperature. Even if they survive a temperature increase caused by constant floods of hot water, their behaviour may change.

The heedless pollution of Canada's waterways with industrial wastes has serious consequences for our entire fish population. Mass die-offs are a grim reminder that a life underwater is a precarious one which can see a whole generation, or even an entire species, wiped out by the thoughtlessness of man.

135

The lower forms of life – parasites and bacteria – tend to respond and adapt most readily.

'Thus, while fish congregate readily at the warm outlet from a power station because of increased food growth there,' said a federal report, 'like children at a free candy store they soon get sick.'

Specifically, pollution is taking its toll of species all over Canada. In some parts of Ontario, the lake trout's future is threatened, partly because of agricultural runoff which causes silting in traditional spawning areas, and partly because of sewage discharges from shoreline cottages.

The Winnipeg goldeye, depleted by overfishing in Lake Winnipeg, was wiped out by pollution in the South Saskatchewan River. The silvery minnow, known in Canada only in the Milk River of southern Alberta, is deemed 'rare and endangered,' partly because of siltation.

The blue walleye, a subspecies of the normal yellow walleye, may now be extinct in Lakes Erie and Ontario, reports Dr McAllister, 'probably due to pollution.' The deepwater cisco, once known in Lake Huron, hasn't been seen since 1951. The longjaw cisco may still exist deep in eastern Lake Erie – or then again it may be extinct. Nobody knows for sure.

Perhaps the gloomiest examples of what can happen to a region's water and marine life are in the Atlantic provinces. In the 1950s, for example, more than half of New Brunswick's forests were sprayed with DDT against the spruce budworm. It also killed young salmon at a rate of 50 to 98 per cent. DDT was finally discontinued after many years.

In 1970, a federal fisheries official reported that 25 per cent of the shellfish beds along shores in the Atlantic region were contaminated by sewage. A year later many Nova Scotia swordfishermen went out of business when the mercury content in swordfish was found unacceptable for health standards in most countries. (Subsequently, a few countries have been accepting swordfish with a higher mercury content.)

Once famous as a Canadian delicacy, smoked Winnipeg goldeye is now rarely available. This fish has been almost depleted in Lake Winnipeg, from which it gets its name.

136

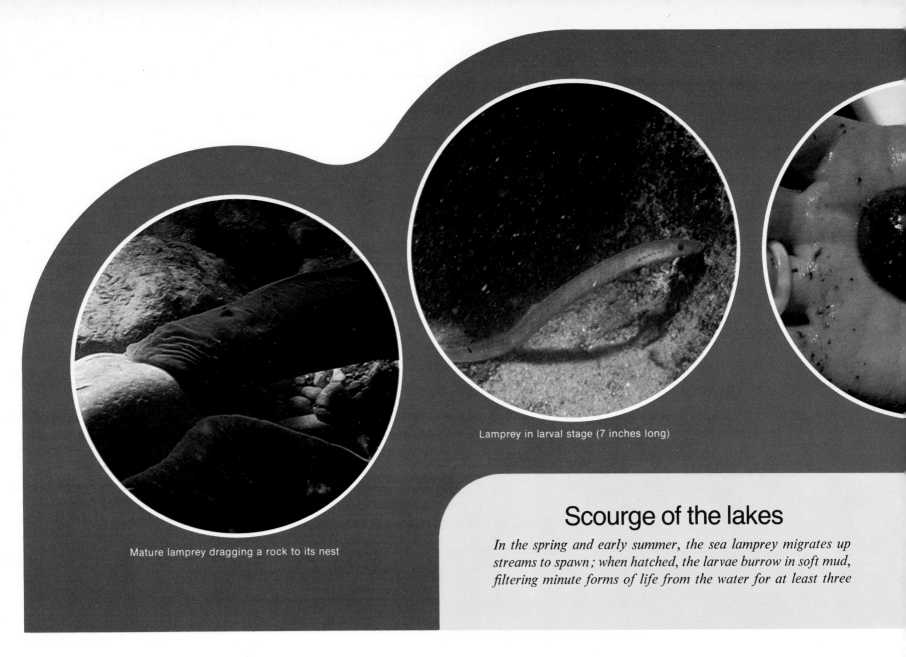

Mature lamprey dragging a rock to its nest

Lamprey in larval stage (7 inches long)

Scourge of the lakes

In the spring and early summer, the sea lamprey migrates up streams to spawn; when hatched, the larvae burrow in soft mud, filtering minute forms of life from the water for at least three

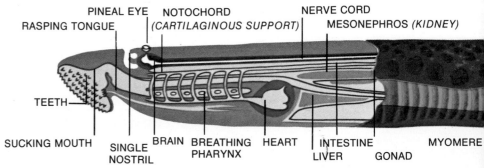

PINEAL EYE   NOTOCHORD   NERVE CORD
RASPING TONGUE   *(CARTILAGINOUS SUPPORT)*   MESONEPHROS *(KIDNEY)*

TEETH

SUCKING MOUTH   SINGLE   BRAIN   BREATHING   HEART   INTESTINE   MYOMERE
NOSTRIL   PHARYNX   LIVER   GONAD

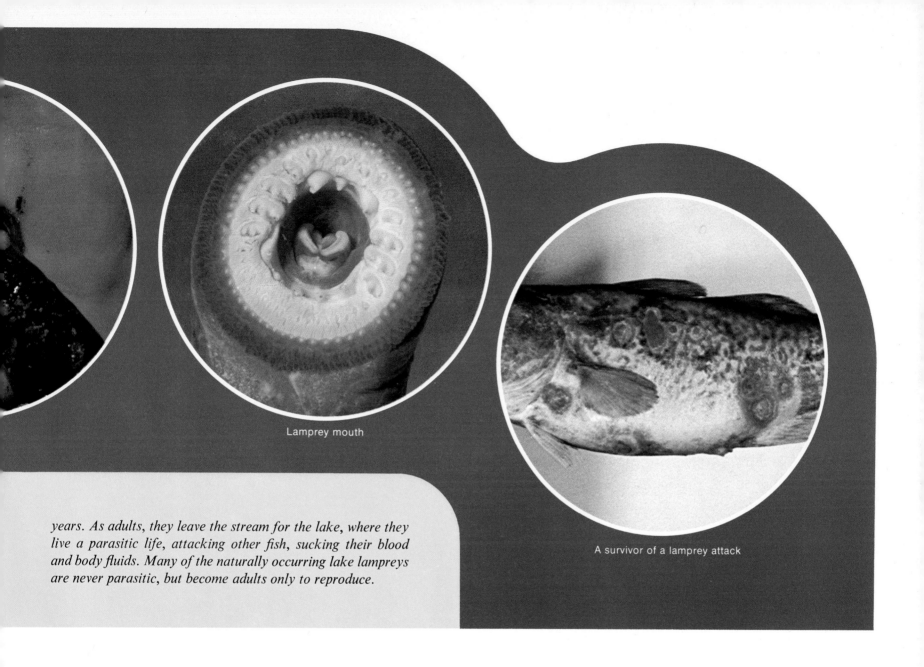

Lamprey mouth

A survivor of a lamprey attack

years. As adults, they leave the stream for the lake, where they live a parasitic life, attacking other fish, sucking their blood and body fluids. Many of the naturally occurring lake lampreys are never parasitic, but become adults only to reproduce.

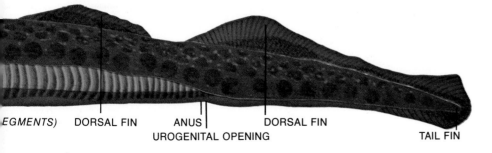

EGMENTS) DORSAL FIN ANUS DORSAL FIN
UROGENITAL OPENING TAIL FIN

The silvery Atlantic whitefish, known only off southern Nova Scotia, is endangered by heavy fishing and by power developments, says Dr McAllister. Pollution in the St John River, which is dubbed a 'killer' by some locals, has on several occasions blocked the upstream migration of Atlantic salmon. Also in the St John, wastes and poisons from pesticides and industry and municipal sewage are endangering the shortnose sturgeon. Known in Canada only in this river, the shortnose sturgeon grows up to three feet long over a period of fourteen years. But fourteen years in the St John River is tantamount to a death sentence. Although anti-pollution measures were begun when the river's sickness was fully realized, a 1973 study reported that the dissolved oxygen level in some sections was nearly zero. For a bottom-feeding fish such as the sturgeon, that's lethal.

There is no mystery to pollution. We know the causes, effects, and cures. But unless governments, municipalities, industries, and individuals recognize that current action is far too feeble, we may pass the point of no return.

---

25 THE CHAIN-REACTION OF POLLUTION

There are a few glimmers of hope in the dreary record of waste and destruction. One, oddly, comes from the oil industry. A geologist for the Sohio Petroleum Company in the U.S. claims, after twenty-three years of studying marine ecology in the Gulf of Mexico, that drilling platforms in the Gulf actually foster fish life, by setting up artificial reefs. Algae grows on the legs of the drilling platforms anchored in the sea. Shellfish and small fish congregate next. Bigger fish move in. Eventually 'a whole new and flourishing biological community is created.' If the same proves true of other offshore drilling operations, it would pay off some of the debts that the oil industry owes to the environment.

Fish culture of various kinds is also a lively possibility for the future. Striped bass and shad eggs hatched on the U.S. east coast have been successfully transferred to rivers in California. Russia has transplanted Pacific salmon to Euro-

pean waters. Herring have been shifted from the Baltic to the Aral Sea.

Scotland has fertilized several lochs with chemicals, resulting in rich growths of plankton and thriving schools of plaice. In Mississippi, a publicly owned corporation hatches fifty million catfish a year on forty acres of pollution-free ponds. In Illinois and Wisconsin, trout and salmon are being experimentally raised in waste-water lagoons.

British Columbia reports encouraging results with artificial spawning runs for salmon. For example, a hydro-electric development on a tributary of the Lower Fraser had reduced the pink salmon spawning runs from highs of 5,000 to barely 400. The artificial run brought the fish population back to full strength.

Lake Michigan offers another story of successful management. In the 1920s, it was healthy and rich in aquatic life. Then some sea lampreys slipped in via the rebuilt Welland Canal, and systematically cleaned out the Mackinaw trout, whitefish, burbot, steelhead trout, lake herring, and perch. With those predators gone, there was an explosion of ale-

Fish farms

In the 1850s, Canada was the North American pioneer in raising fish from artificially fertilized eggs. The eggs are stripped from the female (left), fertilized, and protected. Salmon and trout eggs in the eyed stage can be shipped without difficulty, and have been widely distributed all over the world.

Various forms of fish management are being tried by government agencies in all parts of the world, in an effort to re-establish balances and increase populations of certain species.

The Canadian government offers free advice and consultation to farmers wishing to stock ponds or creeks, or wishing to construct farm ponds. One particular program, which has received enthusiastic participation by citizens, is the federal government's experimental program for pothole fishing in the prairies. With free advice from the government's Freshwater Institute in Winnipeg, pothole fishermen obtain a permit, buy fingerlings each spring, stock their ponds (right), and by autumn can expect a healthy catch of twelve-inch trout (below).

wives, a small fish of little commercial value – and of no interest to the lampreys, which swam over to Lake Superior.

In 1955, Canada and the United States established a joint commission to deal with the problem. Dow Chemical came up with a compound that would kill lampreys but in proper proportions not harm other fish. A million coho salmon eggs were flown in. Coho eat alewives. The alewive population levelled off and the lake became relatively healthy again.

The most intriguing venture in Canadian fish management today is pothole fishing on the prairies. With free advice from the federal government, which operates an experimental program in Manitoba, some 1,500 people in the three provinces are raising rainbow trout in 1,800 natural lakes and farm dugouts.

Rainbow are ideal for the scheme because they are easy to raise, grow fast, and can withstand reasonably warm water temperatures in summer. Pothole fishermen, armed with a government permit, buy fingerlings each spring (prairie winters are too severe for trout to survive in shallow waters) and by autumn can mosey out to the back forty to harvest a crop of twelve-inch trout.

Most people, says L. A. Sunde of the government's Freshwater Institute in Winnipeg, 'are satisfied to recover their costs and have a big batch of trout in their freezer in the fall.' But fish farming could become a commercial venture on the prairies some day.

Pothole fishing demonstrates, for one thing, how readily nature will respond in the unlikeliest places, given a chance.

The introduction of coho salmon (below) *into the Great Lakes has resulted in a fisherman's dream. The ability of the coho to reproduce naturally, combined with its seeming ability to survive sea lamprey attacks, bodes well for its future in fresh waters. Stocks of deepwater ciscoes or chub* (right), *once a plentiful fish in the Great Lakes, have been depleted greatly by commercial fisheries and sea lamprey attacks.*

It is a rare opportunity, too, for the individual actually to take a hand in replenishing one of our resources. Unfortunately, private citizens cannot personally nurse the haddock or Atlantic salmon or shortnose sturgeon back to normal numbers.

But each of us can, at least, insist that governments revise their priorities. We can demand of our legislators that industries be *made* to stop polluting; that municipalities be *made* to clean their sewage; that sea-going vessels be policed and fiercely penalized for dumping.

Is it worth the effort? Is it worth the expense that it will entail for all of us? Of what importance *are* fish, other than on the dinner table?

For one thing, they *belong* here, as much as any of us. With other living things they are, as a wise scientist once put it, 'our only companions in an infinite and unsympathetic waste of electrons, planets, nebulae and stars.' They are part of the delicate intricate chemistry known as life-on-earth. Knowingly to destroy any species, so long and painfully created by evolution over the centuries, is a wanton act.

As the current caretakers of this planet, we have a moral obligation to hand it on to our successors in good repair. More than a hundred years ago, Henry David Thoreau wrote in his *Journal*, 'I take infinite pains to know all the phenomena of the spring, for instance, thinking that I have here the entire poem, and then, to my chagrin, I hear that it is but an imperfect copy that I possess and have read; that my ancestors have torn out many of the first leaves and grandest passages, and mutilated it in many places. I should not like to think that some demi-god had come before me and picked out some of the best stars. I wish to know an entire heaven and an entire earth.'

If we do not yearn for an entire sea, for reasons of conscience and aesthetics, we should do so out of sheer self-interest. Costeau, among others, has warned that ocean life may be totally destroyed in the foreseeable future, if we follow our present polluting path. Some of the chain-reaction that would result is fairly obvious: if sea creatures died, all the birds and animals that depend on those creatures would also perish.

But there is more. Plankton – microscopic floating plant and animal life that is so vital to the fish – also contributes some 70 per cent of the world's oxygen. Some biologists fear that if the oceans become stagnant pools, *all* life on earth will die.

If this is true, or even a remote possibility, simple sanity dictates that we must save the fishes and the waters – to save ourselves, before our time runs out.

ROBERT COLLINS

GEOLOGIC TIME SCALE

TIME	ERA	PERIOD	EPOCH	THE ASCENT OF LIFE:
	CENOZOIC	QUATERNARY	PLEISTOCENE	
		TERTIARY	PLIOCENE	
			MIOCENE	
			OLIGOCENE	
50			EOCENE	
			PALEOCENE	
100	MESOZOIC	CRETACEOUS	UPPER	
			LOWER	
150		JURASSIC	UPPER / MIDDLE / LOWER	
200		TRIASSIC	UPPER / MIDDLE / LOWER	
250	PALAEOZOIC	PERMIAN	UPPER / MIDDLE / LOWER	
300		PENNSYLVANIAN		
350		MISSISSIPPIAN		
		DEVONIAN	UPPER / MIDDLE / LOWER	
400		SILURIAN		
450		ORDOVICIAN	UPPER / MIDDLE / LOWER	
500 / 550		CAMBRIAN	UPPER / MIDDLE / LOWER	

MILLIONS OF YEARS

THE ASCENT OF LIFE: 1, *protozoan*; 2, *jellyfish*; 3, *crinoid*; 4, *cephalopod*; 5, *climatius*; 6, *shark*; 7, *brachiopod*; 8, *seed fern*; 9, *dimetrodon*; 10, *brontosaurus*; 11, *plesiosaur*; 12, *tyrannosaurus*; 13, *taeniolabis*; 14, *diatryma*; 15, *hyracotylus*; 16, *brontotherium*; 17, *oxydactylus*; 18, *pliohippus*; 19, *mastodon*; 20, *man*.

145

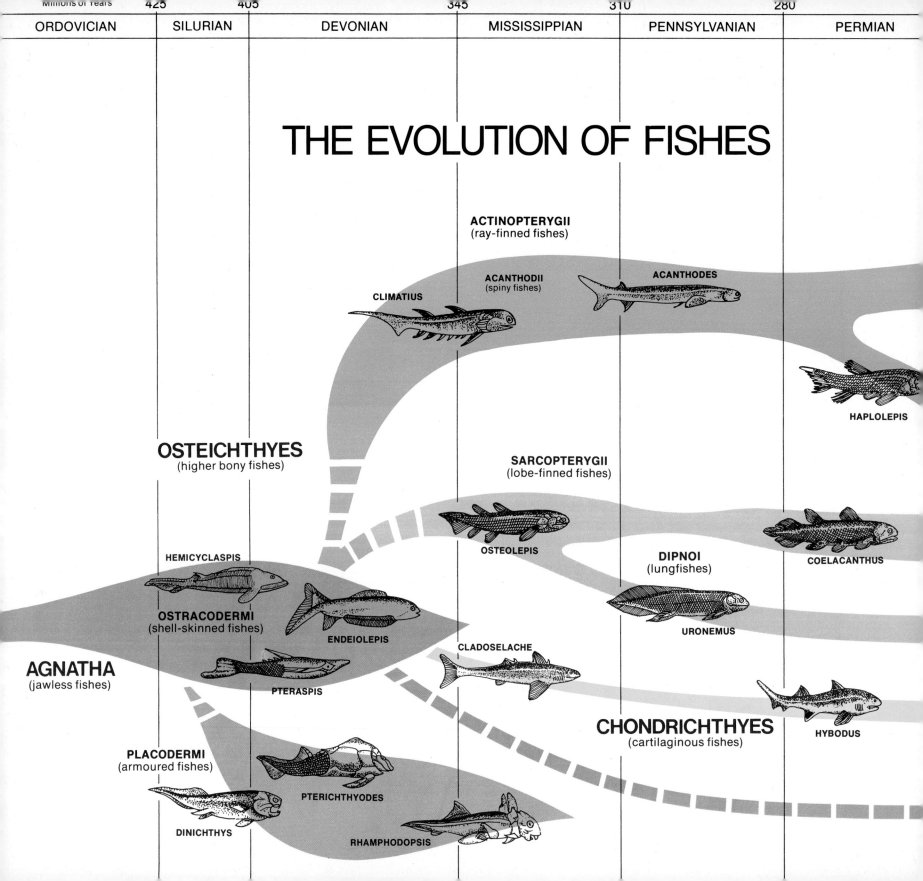

THE EVOLUTION OF FISHES

ACTINOPTERYGII
(ray-finned fishes)

ACANTHODII
(spiny fishes)

ACANTHODES

CLIMATIUS

HAPLOLEPIS

OSTEICHTHYES
(higher bony fishes)

SARCOPTERYGII
(lobe-finned fishes)

HEMICYCLASPIS

OSTEOLEPIS

DIPNOI
(lungfishes)

COELACANTHUS

OSTRACODERMI
(shell-skinned fishes)

ENDEIOLEPIS

CLADOSELACHE

URONEMUS

AGNATHA
(jawless fishes)

PTERASPIS

CHONDRICHTHYES
(cartilaginous fishes)

HYBODUS

PLACODERMI
(armoured fishes)

PTERICHTHYODES

DINICHTHYS

RHAMPHODOPSIS

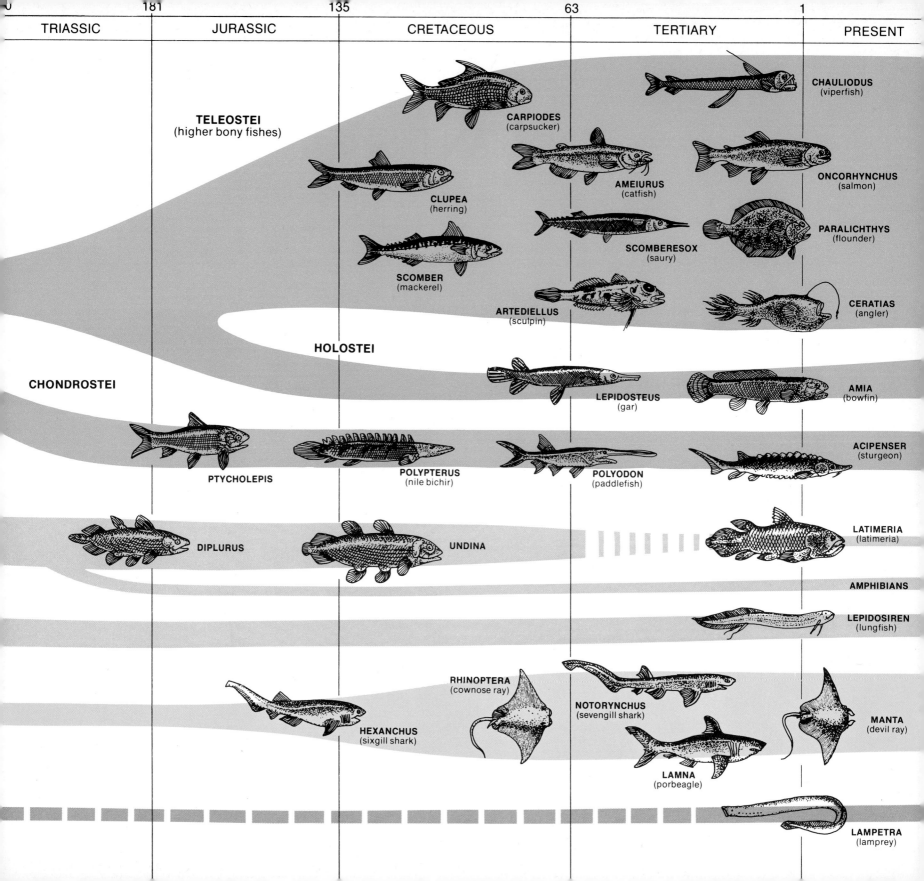

TRIASSIC	JURASSIC	CRETACEOUS	TERTIARY	PRESENT

181   135   63   1

TELEOSTEI
(higher bony fishes)

CHAULIODUS
(viperfish)

CARPIODES
(carpsucker)

AMEIURUS
(catfish)

ONCORHYNCHUS
(salmon)

CLUPEA
(herring)

PARALICHTHYS
(flounder)

SCOMBERESOX
(saury)

SCOMBER
(mackerel)

ARTEDIELLUS
(sculpin)

CERATIAS
(angler)

HOLOSTEI

LEPIDOSTEUS
(gar)

AMIA
(bowfin)

CHONDROSTEI

ACIPENSER
(sturgeon)

PTYCHOLEPIS

POLYPTERUS
(nile bichir)

POLYODON
(paddlefish)

DIPLURUS

UNDINA

LATIMERIA
(latimeria)

AMPHIBIANS

LEPIDOSIREN
(lungfish)

RHINOPTERA
(cownose ray)

NOTORYNCHUS
(sevengill shark)

MANTA
(devil ray)

HEXANCHUS
(sixgill shark)

LAMNA
(porbeagle)

LAMPETRA
(lamprey)

CANADIAN FISHES

The size and habitat of the major fishes illustrated in this book are shown below.

Freshwater fishes

Species	Size	Habitat
smallmouth bass	6-20 inches	cool lakes and streams
rock bass	3-10 inches	cool lakes and large streams
kokanee (freshwater sockeye salmon)	10-24 inches	western lakes
rainbow trout	12-18 inches	variable (freshwater and anadromous)
pike	18-30 inches	warm weedy lakes, ponds, and large slow rivers
common shiner	3-6 inches	mostly in warm, rocky lakes and streams
Arctic grayling	10-20 inches	cold, clear lakes and streams, northwestern Canada and Alaska
lamprey	max. 18 inches	lakes and streams (mostly non-parasitic)
garfish	12-24 inches	reedy backwaters of the Great Lakes
bowfin	12-30 inches	warm, weedy, almost swampy, shallow bays and rivers
carp	12-20 inches	lakes and streams (spawns in warm shallows)
gizzard shad	average 10 inches	Great Lakes, St. Lawrence, eastern seaboard, and Mississippi
johnny darter	1-2 inches	lakes and rivers of moderate to no current, Hudson Bay drainage, Great Lakes, and St. Lawrence
burbot	average 15 inches	deeper lakes in south, cold rivers in north
trout perch	3-4 inches	deep lakes or turbid streams
yellow pickerel	average 13-20 inches	prefer dark waters, central and eastern North America
fathead minnow	2 inches	in Ontario prefers clear waters, but can withstand saline lakes, southcentral and eastern North America
pumpkinseed	1-9 inches	lakes and large rivers, eastern North America
northern pike	18-30 inches	mostly freshwater, some in brackish water, circumpolar in north
muskie	30-50 inches (max. 6 feet)	St. Lawrence, Great Lakes, Ohio River, Wisconsin, and Minnesota
speckled (brook) trout	average 10-12 inches	streams and lakes, but strays into salt water in the east
brown trout	average 16 inches	introduced into North America in 1833, can be anadromous
log perch	3-4 inches	shallow water (4-100 feet) east and central North America
rainbow darter	2 inches	in Canada only in streams entering lakes Ontario, Erie, St. Clair, and Huron
Quebec red trout (subspecies of Arctic char)	15 inches	Quebec lakes
splake (hybrid of speckled and lake trouts)	12-15 inches	prefers shallow waters
bluegill	7-8 inches	shallow, warm water, Great Lakes and south
Winnipeg goldeye	12-15 inches	central North American inland waters, endemic to North America, one relict population in James Bay drainage

deepwater cisco (chub) about 12 inches   15-100 fathoms in lakes Huron and Michigan, not seen in Lake Michigan since 1951

Atlantic fishes

Species	Size	Habitat
eelpout (2 species)	max 13 inches 30-36 inches	Labrador to Bay of Fundy (both species)
northern searobin	to 15 inches	inshore waters from South Carolina to Canada
anglerfish	to 4 feet	shallow water to 500 feet, Gulf of St. Lawrence to Brazil
thorny skate	12-14 inches	sandy muddy bottoms
spiny dogfish shark	to 3 feet	abundant in shallow offshore waters
wolf eel	to 5 feet	deep on dark bottoms, south Labrador to Cape Cod
rock gunnel	9-12 inches	tide pools and shallow rock areas
mackerel	to 22 inches	shore areas both sides of Atlantic, Labrador to Cape Cod
capelin	to 9 inches	shallow to moderate depths, Hudson Bay to Maine
herring	to 17 inches	shallow to mid depths, both sides of the Atlantic

Pacific fishes

Species	Size	Habitat
black banded rockfish	to 2 feet	common to 150 fathoms, central California to Alaska
red Irish lord	to 20 inches	shallow water near shore from California to Bering Sea
starry flounder	to 3 feet	ocean shallows to 150 fathoms, California to Alaska
greenling	to 16 inches	on rocky shores, British Columbia to Bering Sea
plainfin midshipman	to 15 inches	intertidal to 145 fathoms, southern California to northern British Columbia
decorated blenny	to 15 inches	shallow rocky area, Washington to Bering Sea

striped sea perch	to 15 inches	shallow water, Baja California to Alaska
kelp greenling	to 21 inches	shallow water, California to Aleutians
grunt sculpin	to 3 inches	shallow tide pools and rocky areas, California to Bering Sea

Salt/freshwater fishes

Species	Size	Habitat
sea lamprey	10-18 inches (fresh) 15-36 inches (salt)	young live in streambeds. Adults in fresh or salt water are parasitic
alewives	3-10 inches (fresh) 6-18 inches (salt)	open water
threespined stickleback	2 inches	circumpolar, fresh and salt water
smelt	7-18 inches	uncertain taxonomy, possibly occurring on both Atlantic and Pacific coasts, intruded into Great Lakes in early 1900s.
Arctic grayling	12-20 inches (man. 30 inches)	anadromous and landlocked in cold streams, northwestern Canada and Alaska
Arctic char	15-18 inches	northern fish of cold waters, fresh and salt water, circumpolar
American eel	30-40 inches	inland lakes, returns to sea to spawn
coho salmon	to 3 feet	anadromous, southern Alaska to California
sockeye salmon	18-36 inches	anadromous, Pacific coast
chum salmon	to 3 feet	anadromous, southern California to Alaska and Japan
Atlantic salmon	to 60 pounds	anadromous, both sides of Atlantic

Atlantic and Pacific fishes

Species	Size	Habitat
viperfish	to 12 inches	mid depths of oceans 1500-2500 feet
lumpfish	to 2 feet	shallow waters of both coasts

BIBLIOGRAPHY

AUGUSTA, JOSEF and ZDENEK BURIAN, *Prehistoric Sea Monsters*, London: Paul Hamlyn Ltd., 1964

BREDER, CHARLES M., JR., *Marine Fishes of the Atlantic Coast*, New York: G.P. Putnam's Sons, 1948

BROWN, MARGARET, (ed.), *The Physiology of Fishes*, New York: Academic Press, 1957

BURTON, MAURICE, *Under the Sea*, New York: Franklin Watts Inc., 1960

CANADIAN WILDLIFE FEDERATION, *Endangered Wildlife in Canada*, Ottawa: CWF, 1970

CARSON, RACHEL L., *The Sea Around Us*, New York: Oxford University Press, 1961

CLEMENS, W.A. and G.V. WILLEY, *Fishes of the Pacific Coast of Canada*, Ottawa: Fisheries Research Board of Canada, 1961

COCANNOVER, JOSEPH A., *Water and the Cycle of Life*, New York: Devin-Adair, 1958

COLBERT, EDWIN H., *Evolution of the Vertebrates*, New York: John Wiley & Sons, 1969

CURTIS, BRIAN, *The Life Story of the Fish*, Gloucester: Peter Smith, 1962

DE BEER, SIR GAVIN, *Atlas of Evolution*, London: Thomas Nelson & Sons, 1964

EALES, J.G., *The Eel Fisheries of Eastern Canada*, Ottawa: Fisheries Research Board of Canada, Bulletin 166, 1968

ENGEL, LEONARD and THE EDITORS OF LIFE, *The Sea*, New York: Time Inc., 1963

FOERSTER, R.E., *The Sockeye Salmon*, Ottawa: Fisheries Research Board of Canada, Bulletin 162, 1968

HAIG-BROWN, RODERICK L., *Canada's Pacific Salmon*, Ottawa: Department of Fisheries of Canada, revised 1967

HALSTEAD, L.B., *The Pattern of Vertebrate Evolution*, Edinburgh: Oliver & Boyd, 1969

HARDEN JONES, F.R., *Fish Migration*, London: Edward Arnold, 1968

HART, J.L., *Pacific Fishes of Canada*, Ottawa: Fisheries Research Board of Canada, Bulletin 180, 1973

HERALD, EARL S., *Fishes of North America*, Garden City: Doubleday & Company Inc., 1972

HERALD, EARL S., *Living Fishes of the World*, Garden City: Doubleday & Company Inc., 1961

HUBBS, CARL L. and KARL F. LAGLER, *Fishes of the Great Lakes Region*, Ann Arbor: University of Michigan Press, 1947

HVASS, HANS, *Fishes of the World*, London: Methuen & Co, Ltd., 1965

INTERNATIONAL UNION FOR CONSERVATION OF NATURE AND NATURAL RESOURCES, *Red Data Book*, Morges: 1966

KENT, GEORGE C., JR., *Comparative Anatomy of Vertebrates*, New York: McGraw Hill, Inc., 1954

KLOTS, ELSIE B., *The New Field Book of Freshwater Life*, New York: G.P. Putnam's Sons, 1966

KYLE, HARRY M., *The Biology of Fishes*, Neptune: TFH Publications, 1971

LAGLER, K.F., J.E. BARDACH, and R.R. MILLER, *Ichthylogy*, New

York: John Wiley & Sons Inc., 1962

LANHAM, URL, *The Fishes*, New York: Columbia University Press, 1962

Larousse Encyclopedia of Animal Life, Foreward by Robert Cushman Murphy, London: P. Hamlyn, 1967

LEIM, A.H. and W.B. SCOTT, *Fishes of the Atlantic Coast of Canada*, Ottawa: Fisheries Research Board of Canada, Bulletin 155, 1966

LLOYD, TREVOR, 'A Water Resources Policy for Canada,' Ottawa: *Canadian Geographical Journal*, Vol. LXXIII, No. 1, January 1966

LOCKLEY R.M., *Animal Navigation*, London: Barker, 1967

MACCRIMMON, HUGH R. and BARRA LOWE GOTS, *Rainbow Trout in the Great Lakes*, Toronto: Sport Fisheries Branch, Ministry of Natural Resources, 1972

MACDONALD, ROBERT, *Years and Years Ago*, Calgary: Ballantrae Foundation, 1971

MACKAY, H.H., *Fishes of Ontario*, Toronto: Department of Lands and Forests, 1963

MCALLISTER, D.E., 'Rare or Endangered Canadian Fishes,' Ottawa: *The Canadian Field Naturalist*, Volume 84, 1970

MCPHAIL, J.D. and C.C. LINDSEY, *Freshwater Fishes of Northwestern Canada and Alaska*, Ottawa: Fisheries Research Board of Canada, Bulletin 173, 1970

MARX, WESLEY, *The Frail Ocean*, New York: Ballantine Books Inc., 1969

MILNE, LORUS and MARGERY, *The Senses of Animals and Men*, New York: Atheneum Publishers, 1972

MOORE, RUTH and THE EDITORS OF LIFE, *Evolution*, New York: Time Inc., 1962

NATIONAL GEOGRAPHIC SOCIETY, *Wondrous World of Fishes*, Editor-in-Chief, Melville Bell Grosvenor, Washington: NGS, 1965

NORMAN, J.R. and P.H. GREENWOOD, *A History of Fishes*, New York: Hill & Wang, Inc., 1963

OMMANNEY, F.D., *A Draught of Fishes*, London: Longmans, 1965

OMMANNEY, F.D. and THE EDITORS OF LIFE, *The Fishes*, New York: Time Inc., 1963

ORR, ROBERT T., *Animals in Migration*, New York: The Macmillan Company, 1970

PERLMUTTER, ALFRED, *Guide to Marine Fishes*, New York: New York University Press, 1961

ROMER, ALFRED S., *The Vertebrate Story*, Chicago: University of Chicago Press, 4th edition, 1959

ROULE, LOUIS, *Fishes, Their Journeys and Migrations*, New York: W.W. Norton & Co., 1933

SCOTT, W.B., and M.G. SCOTT, *A Checklist of Canadian Atlantic Fishes*, Toronto: Royal Ontario Museum, Life Sciences Contribution 66, 1965

SCOTT, W.B. and E.J. CROSSMAN, *Checklist of Canadian Freshwater Fishes*, Toronto: Royal Ontario Museum, Life Sciences, Miscellaneous Publications, 1969

SCOTT, W.B. and E.J. CROSSMAN, *Freshwater Fishes of Canada*, Ottawa: Fisheries Research Board of Canada, Bulletin 184, 1973

SCOTT, W.B., *Freshwater Fishes of Eastern Canada*, Toronto: University of Toronto Press, 1955

STREET, PHILIP, *Animal Weapons*, London: MacGibbon & Kee, 1971

STORER, TRACY I. and ROBERT L. USINGER, *General Zoology*, New York: McGraw-Hill Inc., 4th edition 1965

SWEENEY, JAMES B., *A Pictorial History of Sea Monsters and Other Dangerous Marine Life*, New York: Crown Publishers Inc., 1972

WALDEN, HOWARD T., *Familiar Freshwater Fishes of America*, New York: Harper & Row, 1964

WALTER, HERBERT E., and LEONARD P. SAYLES, *Biology of the Vertebrates*, New York: The Macmillan Company, 1959

WEISZ, PAUL B., *The Science of Zoology*, New York: McGraw-Hill Inc., 1966

WELLS, A. LAURENCE, *The Observer's Book of Freshwater Fishes*, London: Frederick Warne & Co., 1961

WELLS, A. LAURENCE, *The Observer's Book of Sea Fishes*, London: Frederick Warne & Co., 1958

YAPP, W.B., *An Introduction to Animal Physiology*, London: Oxford University Press, 1960

YOUNG, J.Z., *The Life of Vertebrates*, London: Oxford University Press, 1962

ZIM, HERBERT S. and HURST H. SHOEMAKER, *Fishes*, New York: Golden Press, 1956

INDEX

ACKNOWLEDGEMENTS AND CREDITS

The authors and editors of this volume wish to thank the following organizations and individuals whose assistance with the text and illustrations made this book possible: Dr E. J. Crossman, Department of Icthyology, Royal Ontario Museum; J. P. Cuerrier, Canadian Wildlife Services, Ottawa; Dr Gordon Edmund, Department of Paleontology, Royal Ontario Museum; Dr Alan Emery, Department of Icthyology, Royal Ontario Museum; Fisheries Research Board of Canada, St Andrews, N.B.; Joseph Gough, Fisheries and Marine Information, Environment Canada, Ottawa; Dr C. G. Gruchy, National Museum of Natural Sciences, Ottawa; Dr Harold Harvey, Department of Zoology, University of Toronto; B. LeDrew, Fisheries and Marine Information, Environment Canada, Ottawa; Dr J. MacInnes, Toronto; Dr D. E. McAllister, Curator of Fishes, National Museum of Natural Sciences, Ottawa; P. D. Murray, Fisheries and Marine Information, Environment Canada, Ottawa; T. F. Pletcher, Vancouver; Dorothy Revel, New York Zoological Society, New York; Marsha Rodney, Royal Ontario Museum, Toronto; Dr Loris Russell, Royal Ontario Museum, Toronto; Dr W. B. Scott, Department of Icthyology, Royal Ontario Museum, Toronto; L. A. Sunde, Freshwater Institute, Winnipeg; Mark Wilson, University of Toronto; W. D. Woods, Upper Canada College, Toronto.

Where more than one picture appears on a page, the order of credits is left to right, horizontal separated by commas, vertical separated by semi-colons.

Cover	Mont Richardson
Back Cover	Jack Youngblut
1	Jack Youngblut
2,3	John D. Clarke
4,5	T. W. Hall
6	Ario Gatti
9	Bill Brooks
10	Courtesy of Royal Ontario Museum, Toronto
13	Rene Zamic
14,15	W. Carrick
15	T. F. Pletcher, Phil Edgell, J. B. MacInnes
16	Larry Bell
17	Bruce Coleman Associates, T. F. Pletcher
19	Vancouver Aquarium; National Museum of Canada, Ottawa
20	Bill McLennan
21	Mark Wilson; Mark Wilson, Mark Wilson
22	T. F. Pletcher
23	Bruce Coleman Associates, T. F. Pletcher, T. F. Pletcher; W. Carrick, T. F. Pletcher, C. C.

	Lindsey; T. F. Pletcher, T. F. Pletcher, T. F. Pletcher
24	Rick Mason, Jack Youngblut; Alan Hook, R. G. Long
27	Vancouver Aquarium, T. F. Pletcher; T. F. Pletcher
28	Jane Burton, Bruce Coleman Associates
29	T. F. Pletcher
31	T. F. Pletcher; Gordon McLean
32	Bill Brooks
34	T. W. Hall
34,35	T. W. Hall
36	Frances Westman
39	Rene Zamic
40	Robert Young
41	Fisheries Research Board, St. Andrews, N.B.
42	Robert Young
43	Maxime St-Amour
44,45	Vlasta van Kampen
46	Robert Young, Mont Richardson; Montreal Aquarium
47	Montreal Aquarium
48	Montreal Aquarium
50	C. C. Lindsey
51	Jerry Kozoriz; Mark Wilson
52	Rick Mason
54	John D. Clarke; L. D. Lehman, Maxime St-Amour
55	T. F. Pletcher
56	Maxime St-Amour
59	David Taylor
60,61	Jack Youngblut
61	Maxime St-Amour
62	Alan R. Emery; Alan R. Emery; Alan R. Emery; Jack Youngblut
63	Maxime St-Amour
64	FRB, St. Andrews, T. F. Pletcher
65	T. F. Pletcher
66	T. F. Pletcher
67	T. F. Pletcher, T. F. Pletcher; T. F. Pletcher, T. F. Pletcher
68,69	Vlasta van Kampen
68	Maxime St-Amour
68,69	T. F. Pletcher
71	Mont Richardson; Mont Richardson, Mont Richardson
72	Glen Loates; Ronald Orenstein; Alan R. Emery; Jack Youngblut
74	Jack Youngblut
75	Maxime St-Amour
76	Jack Youngblut
76,77	Glen Loates
78,79	Vlasta van Kampen
80	Mont Richardson; Ario Gatti
81	Ario Gatti; Mont Richardson
82	Alan R. Emery
83	Ario Gatti
84	Maxime St-Amour
85	John D. Clarke
87	Allan Hook
88	L. D. Lehman
89	Charles Doucet
90	L. D. Lehman
91	John D. Clarke
92	T. F. Pletcher
93	T. F. Pletcher
94	C. C. Lindsey
94,95	C. C. Lindsey
96	Maxime St-Amour; Maxime St-Amour
97	W. Carrick; Alan R. Emery
98	T. W. Hall
100,101	Jerry Kozoriz
102,103	Dennis Noble
104	British Columbia Government
107	Jane Burton, Bruce Coleman Associates
108,109	Gordon McLean
109	Mont Richardson
111	Maxime St-Amour
112	FRB, St. Andrews
112,113	Maxime St-Amour
114	T. W. Hall
115	T. W. Hall; T. W. Hall

This book was produced entirely in Canada by:
Mono Lino Typesetting Co. Limited: *Typesetting;* Herzig Somerville Limited: *Film Separation*
Ashton-Potter Limited: *Printing;* T.H. Best Printing Co. Limited: *Binding*
Typefaces: Times New Roman and Helvetica. Paper: 64 lb. Georgian Offset Smooth

Printed in Canada